Slip Roads & Off Ramps

- Writing from Castlemilk -

ACKNOWLEDGEMENTS

The book was funded by the South East Area Management Committee of Glasgow City Council and supported by Castlemilk Fringe.

The post of Writer in Residence was funded by Glasgow City Council Libraries Department and the Scottish Arts Council.

Published by:	CUTTING TEETH
Edited by:	Dilys Rose
Cover Photo by:	Ruziah Mohd Nor
Typeset and Printed by:	Campsie Litho Ltd

CONTENTS

TITLE	AUTHOR	PAGE
Get your tongue out a ma cheek	*John McGinty*	*1*
Greater Universal Stores		2
What Cherry Tree?		3
The Poet Soldiers		4
Politics in Everything		5
Slip Roads and Off Ramps	*Eileen Hart*	*6*
Nothing to do, Nowhere to play	*Ruziah Mohd Nor*	*8*
Christmas Gifts		9
Acapulco Blues	*John McGarrigle*	*10*
History Lesson	*Lesley Benzie*	*17*
Mi Body		19
Pizen Streams		20
Lost		22
The Mornin Efter		23
With any luck I might Just Make It	*Teresa Meagher*	*24*
Rumpelstiltskin	*Jackie Hodgman*	*25*
The 7.30 to Aberystwyth		26
Matinee Performance	*Jim Craig*	*29*
Late Night Bus		30
Seconds Out		31
Waste	*Michael Geddes*	*32*
Dreams of a Small Dog	*Peter Arthur*	*39*
Vampires		40
Straight Jacket Racket		40
Air Drop		41
Windows	*Rosina Gilmour*	*42*
The Inscription		43
Wu'll no be long	*Alex Potts*	*48*
The Release of...		49
Mr Inside		50
Growing Old	*Christine Stewart*	*51*
Scrambled Eggs	*G.L. Buglass*	*52*
Body Language	*Eileen Hart*	*53*
The Journey Back	*David Pearce*	*55*
Echoes		56
The Waiting Game	*Margaret Millmaker*	*57*
Mary		57
Private War		58
Oil	*Colette Coen*	*59*
The Smugglers Arms	*Thomas Anderson*	*64*
In My Room	*Austin Docherty*	*66*
Highrise		67
Living Book	*Alex Telford*	*68*
Ambition	*James Hunter*	*75*
Anguish		75
Who Cares?		76
Raintown	*Mary Maghee*	*77*
Environmentally Friendly	*Cath Craig*	*79*
Glasgow's Alive		80
Out of the Darkness		81
Cardboard Box Hotel	*Eddie Graham*	*84*
Looking Back on Tomorrow		85
2 Haiku	*Christine Quarrell*	*86*
Ma's Here		86
Sexism		86
Working Class Woman		87
Female		88
Gynae	*Dilys Rose*	*89*

INTRODUCTION

When I first came to Castlemilk in September 1992, I was told there were plenty of writers here. Good, I thought, I'll be busy from day one, reading manuscripts, setting up writers' groups and so on. 'But there are writers' groups. We've had them for years,' I was told. Okay, so it's a big place, the more the merrier, I thought. I'll just get some publicity together and the rest will fall into place. Needless to say, I was wrong about that. Castlemilk people can be suspicious of incomers, particularly those dragging fancy titles with them. 'Writer-in-*Residence*? But you live in Edinburgh, don't you?'

Things were quiet at first. Apart from tracking down as many people as I could and repeating my job description until I was saying it in my sleep, I chewed my nails and wondered why I was here. 'Don't worry,' I was told, 'You'll soon have plenty to do.' And sure enough, people began to call in. By January I had enough regular visitors to set up a new evening writers' group based at the library and a second group is soon to start up.

If there are things which Castlemilk people have in common, they are reticence, generosity of spirit and tenacity, all essential to anyone who wants to write. Writers' groups can breed other, less attractive traits but I've seen no sign of those here. Everyone I've come across has been, in a real sense, supportive of each other. I don't mean that they offer some kind of bland pat on the back, more of a gentle kick in the right direction.

The stories and poems here are from a wide variety of people of all ages and stages. Some are in writers' groups, others work away on their own. My thanks goes to everyone who contributed to the book, including those whose work doesn't appear. A special thanks is due to Tommy McKeown and the library staff who have gone out of their way to help me in my work, and to Fionna Warren, at Glenwood Annexe, who put all the material on the computer.

So, welcome to **SLIP ROADS & OFF RAMPS**. Hope you enjoy the book as much as I do.

Dilys Rose
Writer-in-Residence
Castlemilk Library
October 1992

JOHN McGINTY

GET YOUR TONGUE OUT A MA CHEEK

"Brady and the girl looked at each other. There was a long silence."

Is this it? she said, hesitated for a second, then went on,

It started out well, but seemed to peter out a bit towards the end.

Metaphors!

Metaphors! echoed D.

Yes, I ran out of metaphors half-way through.

Mmmn. Where do you get your metaphors?

Woolworth's, said the student. A pound for three.

Ah! That explains it, said D. I get mine from Marks and Spencers. I find they're much more versatile and...

And much more expensive, the student butted in. The thing is, I don't get paid to the 28th and this story has to be in before the twentieth so I couldn't afford the Marks and Sparks.

I see, said D.

A voice from outside broke the silence.

Five for a pound! Five for a pound! Get your metaphors here, five for a pound!

D looked at the student. The student looked at D. D made the doorhandle first, checked her stride to open it and the student piled into her back. Down they went in a heap. D was up first and ran out into Catlemilk Drive with the student close on her heels. Both collided with the metaphor salesman and up in the air went the metaphors.

Meanwhile, back in the room, the rest of the group were playing cards for a packet of metaphors someone had lifted out of D's bag, which she had inadvertently left lying around. Their faces were fixed in concentration.

You could have heard a pin drop.

Into the room came a latecomer.

Evening, he said.

No reaction.

He slapped the Evening Times down on the table. The headline read: 500 TO GO AT MARKS AND SPARKS. "It's the recession," a spokesman said. "There's no escaping it."

Greater Universal Stores

Dear God! Could you please send me
A new body as this one is worn out?

Dear customer, Received your letter
Of the thirty-first. Please find enclosed
A copy of the Spring-Summer catalogue
Along with terms and conditions.
Look forward to hearing from you soon.

Dear God! Although I was pleased with
The catalogue you sent me, I'm afraid
I cannot place an order, as the terms
And conditions are not all suitable
(Too many Though Shalt Nots).

Dear customer, Received your letter
Of the thirty-first. Please find enclosed
A copy of the Spring-Summer catalogue
Along with the terms and conditions,
Look forward to hearing from you soon.

Dear Satan!...

What Cherry Tree?

George
G-E-O-R-G-E
The people of Iraq are innocent
Eh...what?
Read my lips George. I said
Eh...what I can't hear above this noise
I said, We have nothing against the people of Iraq.
You need to speak up. I can't hear myself think for all the noise
Read my lips George. I said, We have nothing against the people of Iraq
Who said that?
You did George
Did I?
You did George...Several times
I thought it sounded familiar...No wonder I'm confused
With all that racket outside...What is it?
I think it's Thousand-pounders
Thousand-pounders?
Yes George
You mean bombs?
Yes George...I think there's some two-thousand-pounders in there as well
Christ almighty what's that whooshing noise?
Cruise missiles George...It's like World War Three out there
Jesus
Don't worry George, we're safe in here
Where are we?
It's an air-raid shelter George
Thank god for that...What's that knocking sound?
What kno...
B-A-N-Ggggg
Wake up
THE GHOST OF WASHINGTON-- Wake up Mr President
There's a Jiminy Cricket at the door for you

The Poet-Soldiers

A soldier's sonnet shed his tears of rage
For everyone who has the eyes to see
The shell-shocked squaddie shuffling in his cage
Devoid of sight - Devoid of liberty.

A soldier's words of pity and concern
Were written down in anger and despair
For a world that never-ever seems to learn
A world that never-ever seems to care

Once "Lions led by donkeys" made their way
To the graveyards of the SOMME and PASSCHENDAELE
Now once a year old soldiers have their day
As eyes disguised as fingers read in braille

The words of WILFRID OWEN and SASSOON
Epitaphs to a generation's ruin.

Politics in Everything

"Keep politics out of sport"

When you are sleeping what do you dream about
Do you have nightmares... What about
Is it life... Is it death?

When you wake in the morning
Take a deep breath... in out in out
That's it. What kind of air is it
Is it polluted... what with
Is it fresh... Where are you?

Get yourself out of bed... that's it
What kind of bed is it
Is it a nice well sprung mattress
With a nice soft eiderdown
A bed on the floor maybe
Or a cardboard box... Where are you?

Have a look outside at the view
Is it a thousand tenements all the same
A housing scheme... a ghetto...
Or acres of green in a privileged area
-----Is it cardboard city?

Why are you up so early
Are you working... What kind of work
Is it hard work... menial work
White collar office work
-----What school did you go to----?

Unemployed... Has the giro come yet
Look in the cupboard... Is it empty
It is... Have a look in the mirror
What colour is your skin
It is, is it? Mmmn...
Well it's back to bed for you.

EILEEN HART

SLIP ROADS AND OFF RAMPS

"Ah get a taxi every day son," said the wee woman as she climbed into the cab, puffing and panting in an attempt to regain her breath.

"That right, hen?"

"Oh, aye, son. Never miss," she went on. "Only the other day ah goat a driver, knows me well, s'took me hame umpteen times." Wonder what his wife said to that? the drive thought wryly. He glanced in his rear view mirror.

"Where to then?"

"Oh did an not tell ye, son?" She gave her destination. "Aye, that driver said, Wan merr run in this cab and it's yours. Funny, eh?"

"Aye. Funny."

"Aye. Ma life's dominated. Slip roads."

The driver's eyebrows shot up. He glanced again in his rear-view mirror.

"Slip-roads and off-ramps, son."

"That right? My, my ..." Better get this one home p.d.q., as the saying went. Trouble. He switched on to automatic pilot and began singing to himself: *"So long boy, you can take my place...".*

"Oot and aboot every day. Taxis. Get tae know the lingo," she continued. "Ma boy - watch that caur son - went for his badge, ye know. Failed three times. Working for - double lane here - wan o thae private hire mobs noo."

"Is he, hen?" said the driver. *"Put ma gun down the war is won ...."'*

"Watch they lights son - but ah tellt him, canny beat the service we get fae yous. Well, ah mean, an canny go aw that looking for phones and change tae bump in them. Fir whit? " Ah'm tellin ye - mind that box junction - they're no ony cheaper. Filter's oan, son."

"Where were you going again, hen?" he had to ask. She'd talked so much he'd forgotten. He decided she was one of those Seen-it-all, Heard-it-all, Nothing-you-can-tell-me people. But obviously a staunch taxi user. Kept him in a job.

"Ur ye in the right lane, son? We're gaun straight oan here. But he likes it well enough ma boy. Gets him oot o ma road onyway." The driver sucked the air through his teeth. It helped him stifle a laugh. Must be like living with a never-ending cabaret, he was thinking. Nearly there.

"First oan the left here, son." He stopped the cab. The brakes gave a disapproving squeal.

"I can't go left, hen. It's a one-way street."

The woman stared at him. For a moment she seemed flabbergasted.

"We're only gaun the wan way, son!"

"Yellow River, Yellow River....."

Ruziah Mohd Nor

Nothing To Do, Nowhere To Play

School is over
summer is here
With so much sun
it should be fun
But I'm not glad
I'm rather sad
For there is nothing to do
and nowhere to play .....

I can't play ball in the front yard
It'll knock a flowerpot, scratch a car
I can't have fun in the backyard
It's so small, my frisbee can't go far.

I won't join my friends clowning around
in the streets, vacant lots and car parks
How I wish for a simple playground
Near enough to play until it's dark.

Castlemilk is transforming phase by phase
The old grey flats have never looked better
Even the bins get brand new hideaways
But children are forgotten by the planner!

So when school's over
and summer is here
I don't feel glad
I feel quite sad
I would much prefer
the short days of winter
for there is nothing to do
and nowhere to play .....

Christmas Gifts

December's the time of the year
When she is gripped by a funny fear
    Her days are restless
    Her nights are sleepless
The Christmas season - it is here!

Oh where will she get the money
To buy those gifts for everyone?
    For daughter - Barbie Benetton
    For son - anything with Bart Simpson
And for parents, siblings, ex-hubby?

But this year's slightly better
She had more to spend, made sure -
    Mint, boxed, still under guarantee,
    She found it extremely easy
To sell the gifts she got last year!

John McGarrigle

Acapulco Blues

Craig sat with his legs dangling over the parapet on the roof watching the small figures milling around below. Quite a crowd had gathered. He cleared his throat and spat, watching the spittle as it caught in the wind to be blown away from the crowd to land somewhere upon the grass of the churchyard.

"Bastards, fuckin missed them."

Some of the teenagers among the crowd were jeering. A small boy on a bike cycled around in a circle, then stopped to stare up at the man on the roof. He clasped his hands at both sides of his mouth to make his voice carry farther.

"Jump ya daft bastard, ya silly cunt, fuckin jump!"

Some of the teenagers among the crowd joined in. Two policemen moved into the crowd and forced two or three of the more rowdy ones to move on. Another policeman collared the boy on the bike and seemed to be giving him a good tongue lashing. The man on the roof smiled and spat once more down upon the people below, this time more accurately. Two or three people among the crowd shouted up at him, as they wiped the phlegm from their coats and jackets. The man ignored them and turned on the ghetto blaster that lay at his side. Shakespeare's Sister blasted into the air.

Stay with me... Stay with meee... You better hope and pray that you'll wake one day back in your own world..."

Craig joined in, singing in his rough gravelly voice. He'd never been a good singer and had always been quite ashamed of the sound of his own voice, but he didn't care who heard him now. A vision of Siobhan dressed in black and silver like in the video of the song flashed into his head. Siobhan's tongue flashed from between her lips, licking around the corners of her mouth. Craig closed his eyes and tried hard to imagine himself lying in her arms.

The voice of Radio One disc jockey Jakki Brambles broke into his thoughts. Jakki was informing her listeners of details of how to nominate someone for her Richard Cranium of the week award. Craig smiled, maybe someone would nominate him for it.

Two policemen were on the roof. The younger of the two made as if to approach the man perched on the parapet. Craig rose to his feet, turning to face the two police officers. He bent over and turned down the volume on his ghetto blaster. The policemen had halted several yards away as Craig poked his finger at them.

"Listen, by the way, any nonsense ooti youz bastards n' you'll go flyin ower this roof wi me."

His finger stabbed out every word. The younger of the two police officers raised his hands in a placating gesture.

"Wait a wee minute mate, let's no get hasty. We're only up here to try and help get yi doon."

"Well yiv wasted yir strength and energy, coz very shortly ah'm flyin aff this roof, n' if any youz two try and interfere you'll be gaun alang wi me."

"Listen, let's cool it mate, c'mon to fuck, this is nay use, You don't want ti end yir ain life like this. Ah mean, think of the mess you'll make when yi land doon there."

The young copper had seen this type of tactic work once in a Clint Eastwood movie.

"Tough Shit," Craig answered, "It won't be me that has ti clean it up. Enniwey, ah'll try no tae land oan the grass."

He turned away from the two police officers and leaned over to turn up the volume on the ghetto blaster, effectively dismissing them and drowning out their voices. The older, more experienced police officer, who had remained silent, turned to his partner and shrugged.

"Let the bastard jump, who cares?"

Jakki Brambles was ranting on about some movie that she'd seen the previous evening. Craig took a deep breath and surveyed the scene before him. One of the two policemen was reporting back to someone on his radio. An ambulance and a team of paramedics had arrived below. Patches of golden sunlight were breaking through the thin layers of cloud that lay over Glasgow, brightening up large areas of the city. Craig sighed as he stared out into space. The thin layer of cloud obscured the tops of the Campsie hills spreading away for miles into the distance. Craig experienced a strange feeling of peace and calm high up here on the roof. He felt divorced from the hustle and bustle of the city that spread far below him. He could see the large towers of Ravenscraig lying far off in the distance. Nearer hand,

and only a couple of miles away, he could see the empty sheds of the Clydebridge steelworks, where he'd worked for several years before being made redundant.

Castlemilk lay spread before him almost like a map of his life. He could see the family house on Ardencraig Road where he'd spent most of his childhood. The church where he'd been baptised lay directly below him. He'd made his first holy communion there. He'd also been married there, and when he eventually jumped he would try and land somewhere within its grounds. At some point later in the week, he would be taken from there to the cemetery where he'd be buried.

Craig thought of his ex-wife, and their three kids. She'd left him several years before, taking the children with her. It was as if the earth had opened up and swallowed them without a trace. The last he'd heard of her she was living somewhere down in London with his ex-best friend. Craig had never dreamed that they would some day part. He cleared his throat and spat once more into the crowd below, smiling at their angry response. More cries of "Jump!" were being hurled upward in his direction.

The theme from "Top Gun" was now blaring from the ghetto blaster.

"You take my breath away..."

Craig liked the song. He turned to keep an eye on the two policemen at his back. The younger officer had edged a bit closer. Craig bent over and once more turned down the volume on his radio. He pointed once again at the police officer.

"Ah fuckin warned you! Don't come another step closer, or you'll be for the high jump alang wi me!"

"Hold it mate. No problem." The policeman took a few paces backward.

"Listen, do you smoke mate?" - The policeman produced a packet of cigarettes from his pocket.

Craig shook his head. "Naw it's bad for yir health."

The policemen couldn't tell if Craig was being ironic, or merely stupid.

"Whit's aw this in aid of enniwey?" The policeman asked.

The older policeman shook his head. "Cause eez a nut job."

Craig laughed.

"Ha Ha, ah might be a nut job, but at least ah'm no a fat ugly bastard like you."

The older policeman's face turned red with anger.

"Listen scum, why don't you go ahead n' jump before yi get pushed. OK?"

"Ach well, if ah get pushed then you'll be joinin me oan the wey doon."
The younger policeman asked Craig his name.

"Craig, mah name's Craig."

"Well listen Craig. You've obviously got problems. Would yi no be better aff discussin them with somebody, maybe a psychiatrist or somethin like that?"

"Nah," Craig shook his head. "Ah'd only drive the poor cunt mad."

"For God's sake Craig, things canny be that bad."

"Listen mate, things might look bad to you, but not to me. As far as ah'm concerned, ah don't see any problem here."

"For Christ's sake Craig! Yir staunin up here oan a roof two hundred feet above the ground, jist aboot to commit suicide. How can you staun there and say with a straight face, yi canny see any problem?"

"Because there isnae any problem. Actually ahm only gonny fulfil a lifelong ambition."

The two policemen looked at each other.

"We've got a real one here!"
The older policeman was curious.

"Tell us aboot it Craig. Whit kinda ambition is it yiv got?"
Craig smiled then grinned.

"Hiv you ever seen films of these guys that live in Acapulco, these sky divers?"
The older policeman looked puzzled.

"Nah, whit is it they get up ti?"

"Well," said Craig, "They climb up these big cliffs 150 or 200 feet high and they dive inti the sea n' catch clams, n' coins, n' things like that. Well that's whit ah want ti day. Ah'm gauny dive aff here!"
The two policemen looked at each other, neither of them believing what they'd both heard. The older policeman looked aghast.

"Yi canny be serious. You mean yir gauny jump aff these flats, simply because yiv seen these guys jumpin aff cliffs oan the telly? There's no even any water doon there. Kin yi no jist go doon to the swimmin baths n' jump aff the dale?"
Craig shook his head and smiled.

"Don't be daft. Ah canny swim, can ah? Ah'd end up droonin."
The older policeman was beginning to lose his temper.

"You're aff yir fuckin heid, ya loony. You'd be better aff jumpin."

Craig turned his back on the policemen, then once more turned up the volume on his ghetto blaster. A small breeze had started up, and it had grown a bit colder, but at least the slight wind was beginning to break up the clouds in the sky. There were more patches of sunlight appearing in different areas around the city.

Craig surveyed the scene before him. He could see the hills and woods of the Cathkin Braes rolling away below him. He'd played there as a child among the ferns and the small streams, and when he was older had made love for the first time among the dark woods that lay along the top. To his left he could see the small primary school that he'd attended as a child. The large housing scheme sprawled before him. Council houses with boarded-up windows were scattered everywhere along the streets where he'd grown up. He could see workmen busy at their jobs renovating the houses in Ardencraig Quad where he'd once lived with his wife and children. He'd given up the house after she'd left, leaving him behind with a mountain of debts. Craig had gone back to live with his parents.They were both dead now. Craig was glad that they weren't alive to suffer the pain of his death.

"Rozalla" was singing from the ghetto blaster.
"Are you ready to fly... To leave this world behind..."

It was nearing time now. The sky was clearing and Craig wanted the sun to be shining when he jumped. He started to dance in time with the music. There was a mixture of cheers and jeers from the crowd below.

"Jump! Ya loony! Jump!"

"Gaun ya headcase!"

"Jump! Ya junkie bastard!"

Craig couldn't hear what they were shouting but he could guess. He spat a few times down at the people below. The two policemen shook their heads.

Craig stumbled and nearly fell, struggling to regain his balance. The two policemen made as if to run towards him. Craig froze them with a stare as he regained his balance. He smiled and turned down the volume on the radio. He looked shaken but inside felt angry. He glanced below him. There was a spiked metal fence around the chapel grounds. He shivered at the thought of landing on top of it.

"Nearly had it there boayz, eh? Thought ah wiz a gauner!"

"For Christ's sake Craig! Call it a day. Come doon wi us n' we'll see that yi get help. Don't be a fool." The younger policeman had grown white in the face. Craig smiled.

"Don't worry, the sun's no oot yet. Ah canny jump withoot the sun shinin on mi. It widnae be cool."

"There's fuck all cool aboot this, this is jist stupid."

The other policeman interrupted and sneered.

"He's never gonny jump. Look at the wey eez face turned white there when he nearly fell."

Craig sniggered at him, shaking his head.

"You don't know anythin, day yi? Yir so thick it's unbelievable."

The sun had finally come out, lighting up the area around the flats, bringing out the colours in the fields and the bushes that lay below. Craig stretched his limbs and laughed.

"Well lads, it's time for me to go." He smiled once more at the policemen. Jakki Brambles was informing her listeners of how fine a day it was in London.

"Listen Craig, is there anybody we can contact for yi? Maybe friends or family? A wife, yir mother, yir father. Yi must have a family Craig?"

Craig jumped down from the parapet and walked half way across the roof towards the two officers.

"Whit's yer second name, craig?'

"Craig Oani!" He answered with a grin.

"Craig Oani? "The younger policeman wasn't quite sure if he'd heard him right.

"Aye, Oani Kiddin," Craig laughed as he spun on his heels and ran towards the parapet.

The policeman ran and made a dive for Craig's legs, but missed. Craig leapt up on to the parapet and dived high up into the blue sky. The police officer lay upon the roof as a wave of nausea washed over him.

There was a hushed silence from the crowd as Craig sailed out over the roof in perfect imitation of the divers that he'd so worshipped. The sun glistened off his long fair hair tied back in a pony tail. His baggy shirt and trousers billowed and flapped in the wind, and for a second it seemed as if he was suspended in mid air. Craig closed his eyes. He could feel the warmth of the sun on his back, and the wind blowing in his face. For a few moments he was suspended high above the cliffs of Acapulco, and then he was plummeting like a stone towards the clear blue waters below.

He could feel his arms break through the surface of the waves, and then for a brief moment realised it was the branches of the tree that grew in the chapel grounds. Craid crashed hard into the ground. His head twisted at a strange unbelievable angle, and there was a loud, sudden crack that broke the silence. Some people said that it was one of the large branches from the tree that had broken, while others argued that it was the noise of Craig's spine snapping.

For several seconds the crowd remained silent, then someone screamed. One woman fainted, and collapsed on the ground, while another crossed herself and turned away.

The small boy on the bike gave a round of applause..

"Well done big man," the boy muttered, then cycled away.

The crowd was already starting to disperse.

LESLEY BENZIE

HISTORY LESSON

I ken a story aboot yer life
Hewn as hard as yer granite toon steen
Born the wonderboy
O a wild bewitchin gypsy queen
Beauty fixed only soul deep
And in sepia memories
Years maddening her black eyes
Bent groundward
Wi body's burden o birthins
Miscarriage o life an justice
Bearin still a rich harvest -
Eight loons an quines raised
On poor pickins
O fish brie and porridge
Her life pined and pawned
Alang wi yer Da's Sunday suit
Rarely needed
Fan ye're an absentee at sea
A rough and ruddy trawlerman
Infrequent visitor to the land
Lording still wi a mere fish fry
Present jist lang enough
Tae dip his rod,
Catch her aff guard again,
Plant his seaman's semen
Between sheets and booze bouts.
Yer smert sea-green eyes learned
Well and quick tae despise, spying,
As he stole awa her life,
Daein as she was bidden,
Leavin her wi bairns
Tae fend and fail for

In a twa-roomed midden
Facing shameful the poor parish rebuke
And gut wrench o hungry looks.
Only dreamin freedom
In furtive bauble-buying sprees
At tinkers' marts,
Concealin worthless idiosyncracies
Beneath the bed wi her bleak trackle.
Her tragedy - and that o mony -
echoed in yer youthful mission
spawnin an spurrin owerbearin ambition
tae rise above the streetwise debacle.
Ye worshipped yer ma but despised her life
determined tae find the perfect wife
an be the perfect husband.
Ye'd lead the way, she'd obey,
work day an night on yer fight
fae rag and bone tae riches.
An though cliver ye be,
ye winted mair fer me
than jist that worthy trait.
Bit comfort aye comes late.
I watched ye chase yer tail, an fail,
' cause ye chased a dream
That wid fill yer pouches
But niver mend
Yer unfilled pauper's heart
That tethered ye tae failure,
makkin sure ye'd nae be free
nor stem the tide o yer history.

Mi Body

Mi body's the place I live
it's nae new
neither modern marled brick
nor hi-tech
It's alder 'n softer
big blonde sandstone
rough edges smoothed
far storms hiv' cut 'n sharpened
their teeth
'n love blown awa' the stoor
leavin mottled autumn colours
far ah've absorbed the truth
veiled in rollin scree
that jeelt mi tae the core
Far ah've hid a lifetime tae explore
the myths 'n ghosts that haunt
this quine's hoose
Strong foundations, at the heart
o a daughter
buried alive
deep, under expectations
that ah would'nae live up tae
cause ah'd watched through
mi windaes
at the hoose o mi mither
wi each re-decoration
grown derelict o spirit
the fruits o 'er flooer beds
trumped under fit
as she played 'er part
o little girl-wife
niver ownin 'er life
or 'er body
the place she dwelt

A design similar tae mine
that ah LEARNED TAE HATE
Bit nae too late
ah stopped the neglect
pulled back the blindin
curtains o' lies
let in the air 'n sun
tae dry the tears
warm the nooks 'n crannies
far ah hid 'n found safety fae the world
openin up tae welcome in
past, present 'n future
tae meet 'n find peace
in mi body, mi hame.

Pizen Streams

Pizen streams conspire aginst mi, plooin ruts doon cheeks once apple reid, stiffled tears strainin the fetters o' a dam,dammin a ragin river.

The surface still, father frozen. Decades pass.

The undertow echoes in a wirlie, trappin the pretty picture - a quinie pullin at the coat-tail, priggin, Daddy Daddy please stop.

Stopped deid in ma tracks, again, forced tae bear witness tae a bleed stained han, fingerin shudders doon the re-invented spine 'n book skin o ma life. Yir presence grips ma insides, teerin back the well-healed scar tissue, hidden ahind ma perfected armour. An ah'm back there, siven year aul, eyes 'n nose poorin, mooth open as wide as ma heed, screamin atween each gaggin breath tae get the terror oot. An ah'm pullin fae ma guts at yir coat-tail, mi pleadin daddy, daddy, please stop!

Mergin wi mi ma's screams, till there's a din that's feedin the divil risen in yi, youlin an snarlin.

Yer clenched fists rain bone crunched blows. Snapped gless splinters buryin in ma's skin, burstin wi the strain o'welling bruises, face bleed - gan septic wi the pizen o' yer tongue - as it trickles, flowin, growin in tae reed rapids rinnin doon, raxin mind fae body droonin in pain, pullin mi under. Bit ah'm haudin on fer grim life tae get ye aff her. Yer bonnie heid turns roon tae me wi a different face: grizzly, yer skin nearly splits, spittin twisted purple mo that canni calm itsel' nor me. Tho' it tries, chokin itself tae a coiled whisper: Whisht noo. Back tae yer bed n yer ain business. The fear maks mi go bit ah cin see there's mair bleed-lettin in yer clenched eyes.

Ma's sobbin again. Hissed curses. Storm whirlin, birlin, belly churnin. Ah'm coontin thunder blows so ah dinna hear their sound or the winded screams. Mi sobs are burried in the pilla that ah hope will suffocate mi now. Bit ah'm nae even deef, nivir mind deid. So ah'm up n' fleein through tae wade in the blood bath far ye've snarled a' yer wrang-placed wrath, turnin her face tae an o'er-ripe fruit, dis-featured, slit eyes weepin, dreepin, bluish, purple, plum blood on her pale dress, crumpled roon a blunt sickle body.

His rage spent, we reaped a' heed, han clutched, sorry bully, dolein guilt, wi the ither han reachin oot, invitin mi bonds o love tae rise n gag mi weepin face. Tears bleed inward, stainin mi innocence, makkin mi sick. Ma's cool, healin hans too busy wi yours; 'n weavin a victim's web, enough tae trap hersel 'n me.

Ah nursed the stunted waif inside me, this lang-term casualty healin, as ah wash awa the pain wi the rain o ragin tears flowin free.

Lost

Willin' disbelief
I look in on the scene o' a crime
softly, I rub sare eyes
some kindness wisnae afore time
Somethin missin fae here
Things are oot o' place
I reach for the bathroom
mi eyes gaze at the black n' yella fleer
Scannin, they stop
on the black an' yella glaze
O the tile, bath surround
They're mi favourite, cause they shine
Fleeting' reflections flash back
distract
Fae mi ma's pale floatin dress
the blotches discharge, dirty puffs
O reed, broon, a bloody mess.
Cald in ma pyjamas, I've seen enough
I cin taste salt
Watch tear draps split the water
shatterin the blood clouds, splatter
The face o' a lost quine.

The Mornin Efter

Ah left a touzled 'n tormented sleep
O'er a gawkit fleer, dragged sma' feet
Tae face a neighbour chappin we'r door
That mornin' efter the night afore.
Am needin tae' see yer ma, she said
I lied that she wis sick in her bed
She looks it me wi eyes o' a hawk
Ah glared back
Through tears that jist wouldnae bide hidden
Mi memory pricked
minding me, mi ma wisnae sick
cause the night afore
screams had seeped and risen
Tae swamp the tenement wa's
Echoes fueled her visit
she took confirmation in ma tears
fainin pity hid her true predatory nature
She says cheerio n' ah'll see ye later
I slammed mi barrier tae public pain
but the blethers that slithered between her an' anither
reached ma ears tae turn again the spit o' shame.

TERESA MEAGHER

WITH ANY LUCK I JUST MIGHT MAKE IT!

A real gipsy, a big solemn woman, with oiled black braided hair told my fortune...said I would live 'till I was 102.

Can't wait..surely when I reach 80, I'll have earned the right to be eccentric.

I mean to wear vulgar purple some days, and the other days scarlet.

Ears drooping with sparkling earings, neck encircled with strings of beads. A floppy hat with flowing ribbon, jewelled winged specs disguising old eyes. Resplendent in long black skirt, sweeping the street, forgetful of hygiene.

The skirt will be a splendid garment,with large pockets to accommodate small items acquired surreptitiously, when shop-lifting sprees become necessary for survival.

But 90! 90 is the undisputed licence to be magnificently obnoxious!

I will sit on the pavement when I feel tired, legs akimbo, spit if I have a mind to.

I will make cheeky remarks to passersby, throw in the odd four-letter word, wait wickedly for reaction.

Will probably be ignored..eyed with amusement..or with discreet exchanges.. like.. "She should be put away." Then I'll display the rude two-finger sign.

Honouring the pavement with my person I might get the offer of..... a warm coat, which I will only accept if purple or red.

On the other hand, a pound note pressed into my palm will be accepted with alacrity.

When it rains I'll wear fur trimmed slippers and, to complete the ensemble, a plastic bag on my head.

For now I'll conform..with reservations..

But when I'm 80, I'll start practicing for when I'm 90,

when I hope to be irrevocably and absolutely obnoxious!

JACKIE HODGMAN

RUMPELSTILTSKIN

Dress rumpled from sitting out so many dances.
Legs like stilts.
Spindly pins.
Big skinny Skinner.
Your parents give them the names to call you.
Lovely wee fat thing. Your mother used to say.
About others.
Wee fat. Wee fat.
It was like a religion with her.
And you gawky and awkward.
At the quali dance and not qualifying for a dance.

And now grown. Middle aged even. And gaining that, now lamented, once longed for weight.

'Oh' my mother says 'And you used to be so nice and thin.'

The Seven-Thirty to Aberystwyth

The sky was a washed-out bluey grey, as if someone had put it into a huge celestial washing machine at the wrong programme and put their denims in along with it. Splurges of whiteness merged into blueness and intertwingled with grey.

My bus was chugging up a hill, the engine labouring in second. Splodges of water dripped down the window and the passengers, maybe four or five of us, shivered in the dreich apathy of seven-thirty on a Monday morning.

The bus bobbed and waved round the narrow country roads and sashayed up and over the hills, occasionally jolting the inert passengers and threatening their barely digested bacon and eggs.

The driver was a thin, pokey-faced wee man of indeterminate age, possibly about fifty or, maybe as young as thirtyish, the sort of man who had never been a boy, or a guy, or a lad.

"Bore da," he said to each alighting or mounting passenger and they would reply in a profusion of yochs.

A primitive, ancient language, which only failed them when they needed to talk about television or physics. Then they had to resort to Greek and Latin.

It was like being in a secret society. They had the magical old words which excluded me. They had a thread from the past of their pagan roots to the Monday morning seven-thirty Borth to Aberystwyth. A direct ley line of heritage and culture and acceptance.

The sun was hidden behind a grey cloud but it had a persistent inclination to shine through, almost as if that were its job, and the sky now looked like something from a Blake painting, or perhaps it was a set of scraps I had when I was wee. Anyway, it reminded me of something which had made a lasting pictorial impression on me when I was young.

On the brow of the next but one hill nestled a white cottage. There were roses round the door and a curl of peat smoke from the chimney. Probably. Actually all I could see at this stage was a white blob but I was so engrossed in my romatic notion of Wales, I filled in any missing or mundane bits with an imagination fired by the Mabinogion.

We stopped - unscheduled and unasked - outside the rural idyll, which in fact, turned out to be a fairly standard house of box-like construction, rendered in roughcast. There were no roses.

The thin-faced driver got out of the cab, walked to the front door and rang the bell. He waited. No reply. He rang again. Somewhere inside the house a dog set up a continuous excited barking. There was no visible sign of life. Just the irritating, incessant racket from the dog. Collie or Labrador perhaps.

The driver disappeared round the back of the house and came back a few minutes later, having had no success except in making the frenzied dog verge on the hysterical.

He took a few steps back and looked at the upstairs windows. No movement. He banged on the door.

At no point did he look round to see the eyes of his passengers viewing this spectacle through the glass. If he had he would have seen less than a dozen, half-awake, pasty faces, as much annoyed as curious.

Work was waiting; we were all still half-asleep, too lethargic to care about the urgency of his mission. And that dog! That unceasing din! Feet were shuffling, impatient sighs escaping from taut little mouths.

He would not give up; he banged on a downstairs window. Tried the handle on the front door. Rang and rang the bell. Surely he would give up. No one could possibly be in. The noise could wake the dead. Abandon hope.

"THERE IS NO ONE AT HOME!" we all bellowed below our breath and willed him to get back on to the bus.

Irritation was beginning to be the dominant mood. How could he be so stupid, so pig-headed? There was no one in!

He gave up at last, returned to the bus and made no remark to the waiting passengers. Maybe there was no phrase, outwith French which would have conveyed his feeling. Something else to be added to the list which contained physics and television. We avoided the disappointment in his eyes, or was it something else?

The bus scrambled over the ups and downs of the country road and our breakfast eggs were once more in danger. As it turned the corner I looked back at the house and saw a curtain move to the side and the thin white face of a woman peer suspiciously from the inch or two of bare glass she had parted in the middle.

I forgot about the unimportant incident on the seven thirty from Borth. Years passed and then someone asked me what like it was living in Wales. I shrugged off the question, reluctant to be drawn. He persevered. Something about his particularly parochial syntax, his determination, my hesitation, not wanting to reveal my ambiguous feelings reminded me of the episode on the bus to Aberystwyth and that bus driver and made me wonder what doggedness drove him on and what awful reluctance held her back.

JIM CRAIG

MATINEE PERFORMANCE

The sun is shining outside
but strong lights beat down
as the actors stand ready
awaiting the start
of the day's performance.

Masked and robed,
their sweat-beaded brows
belie the confident air
which they will display
as the drama unfolds.

While behind the scenes,
the star of the show
is made ready
with lotions and potions
and deep-breathing exercises.

A rush of adrenaline
and the action begins
as the players move
with well-rehearsed precision
towards centre stage.
And this practised skill
with words and deeds
brings new life
to a familiar and
oft-repeated scenario.

The name of Caesar is invoked
and keen-edged knives flash
in bloodstained hands
as the struggle continues.

While away off-stage
an anxious producer
paces a lonely corridor
and smokes while awaiting
the forthcoming message

Which will signal
the end of the drama
and the success of the operation,
"Mother and baby, both well."

Late Night Bus

Amanda her name wis.
Ah heard them say it.
Seven or eight maybe,
wi blonde, blonde hair
in a long, long ponytail
tied up wi' a turquoise ribbon.

Black an' white dance tights
an' a pillar box top
wi her initials on it.
Gold hoops in her ears
an' rings an' bangles
as precious as she wis.

Willow-patterned eyes
sparklin' in the light
cheeks red an' rosy
wi' a sunshine smile.
A wee happy mask o' a face
that wis full o' mischief.

Ye might have expected
the current number wan,
hip-hop, bop, rap 'n' rave

or whatever ye call it
but she wis singing her wee heart oot
jist for her mammy

"Show me the way
to go home,
I'm tired and I
want to go to bed..."

Restored ma faith in the future
an' sent me aff the bus singin' as well.

Seconds Out

Thin, icy, cobalt air, shot through with gold,
pounding pulses and the yellow-brass taste of fear.
Clambering clumsily to wing-strut and spar,
braced against the passage wind of our now powerless dive.
Time immobilised by the Arctic cold of altitude,
each fractured second lingering to simulate a lifetime of anticipation.
Toes - independently alive - clenched within constrictive leather,
mittened fingers grasping, lens-protected eyes scanning.
Nostril hairs stiffen as each breath freezes.
Ears roar and protest at the scream of disrupted air.
Heavy canvas harness, cold, stiff limbs,
the bulk of the parachutes suddenly cumbersome.
The dispatcher hanging from his bar-taut strap,
slipstream-stretched mouth opening with the final command.
GO!! The sound lost in the turmoil,
but too late now to escape
from the months and years of trained and disciplined obedience.
A final, flashing check, the conscious surge of will,
then the stomach-swooping fall into nothing ...

MICHAEL GEDDES

WASTE

Tommy looked around the room. An exact square. Four yards by four yards. Cream paint covered all four walls from ceiling to skirting board, and a single fluorescent tube threw its light over the entire area. Here and there, initials and names had been scratched on the walls. The dark brown floor tiles were dull, the sheen long removed by endless pairs of shoes scuffing the surface. Facing Tommy across the white formica topped desk was a chair, plastic with splayed legs, exactly like the one he was sitting on.

Another stood against a wall. There was no other furniture. A uniformed constable stood by the door, eyes fixed on the small window high above Tommy's head. Tommy wondered why they always stood with their hands behind their backs. He cleared his throat and spoke.

"Any idea how long they'll be?" The constable lowered his eyes. It was the only movement he made.

"Couldn't say."

Tommy lifted the polystyrene cup to his lips, but the coffee had grown cold. With a grimace he put it back on the table. Funny, he thought, it hadn't seemed that long since he last took a sip. Fishing around in his battered denim jacket, he brought out a squashed cigarette pack and some matches. He lit up and sat back in his seat.

Footsteps sounded in the corridor outside and Tommy saw the door handle turn. The two C.I.D. men who had taken him from Joe's house three hours earlier strode into the room. The constable left, closing the door behind him. One of the men half lifted the chair that had been standing by the wall and dragged it across the tiled floor. The noise sounded to Tommy like a wounded animal. They both sat facing Tommy across the table. He couldn't remember their faces. The dry, sickly taste of stale alcohol filled his mouth. The older of the two spoke.

"Since ye probably don't remember when we lifted ye earlier, ah'll tell ye again. This is D.C. Henderson. Ah'm D.S. Lyons". He laid a folder in front of him, and gazed straight at Tommy. "Know why ye're here? Tommy shook his head. Lyons sighed. "Mebbe ye've goat a joab workin' night shift in the abbatoir?"

"Eh?"

"Mebbe ye wur skinnin' a rabbit fur yer dinner?" Henderson's voice was loud and hard. Tommy's eyes flitted between the two faces.

"Whit're ye oan aboot? Whit dae yese mean?" Lyons' voice died almost to a whisper.

"Huv ye looked at yer claes recently son? Notice anythin' unusual? Like mebbe a few red spots?"

Tommy scanned his torn and faded jeans and jacket. Even with the accumulation of stains gathered over a year or more, a few rust-coloured marks stood out. He knew they hadn't been there the last time he'd looked. Lyons pushed the coffee cup towards him, pointing into it.

"There's nae smokin in here son." Tommy's cigarette hissed as it hit the dregs of the coffee. Lyons turned to Henderson. "Get 'im a robe John." Henderson got up and left. Lyons rose from his seat. "Right son, get yer claes aff," Tommy made to speak, but didn't. Lyons put both hands on the table. He was hunched over, close to Tommy's face. Tommy could smell the tobacco on the other man's breath.

"You're in a lot o' touble son. Therrs a sixteen year auld boay lying up in the Victoria Infirmary. Chances are he won't be comin' oot again. Everybody says you put 'im therr. Whit dae *you* say?"

Tommy was finding it difficult to unfasten the buttons on his shirt. The fog in his head was shifting, but not quickly enough. He was allowing himself to get rattled. If only he could have longer to think, to remember.

The door opened and Henderson came in carrying an old, faded blue terry robe. He flung it at Tommy.

"Put that oan an' hurry up." It was clean and had obviously been washed scores of times. It smelled faintly of bleach. Tommy was glad to have the extra time to think. He took several deep breaths as he resumed removing his clothes. His fingers were steadier now. That's it, he told himself. Stay calm. Efter a', it's no' the furst time ah've been here. Take it easy an' get the brain workin'. He felt his confidence returning, slowly.

Tommy was twenty three, and had been in several cells and interview rooms in Glasgow's police stations. Okay, so he liked a good bevvy. Occasionally, somebody wid get their face readjusted. So whit? It widny be the furst time *he* hud been oan the receivin' end. Usually, he wis dishin it oot though, the charges had been dropped, or, if it had gone to court, he'd been admonished. Normally probation. Nae problem. The only worry he had was his mother. He knew she worried about him constantly, and it bothered him. His father had long since left for god knew where. Now she struggled up in Drumchapel, spending half her time trying to fill plates and pay bills, and the other half worrying constantly what her only son was getting himself involved in. Donning the robe, he laid his clothes on the table. Lyons gestured to Henderson and the clothes were stuffed into a bag. Henderson took the bag and left. Lyons sat back in his chair and lit a cigarette.

"Right son, let's hear it."

"Ah thought ye said therr wis nae smokin'?" Lyons leaned across, blowing smoke into Tommy's face.

"That's right, fur you therr's nae smokin."

"Whit aboot a coffee then?" Lyons pushed the cup containing the cigarette butt across the table.

"Finish that if ye like."

There was something in Lyons' attitude that bothered Tommy. Previously in face-to-face confrontations there had been a kind of........... reasoning. This time there wasn't even a hint of understanding in Lyons' voice. Surely they were bluffing. Tommy didn't believe that someone was lying fighting for their life. And yet, there was in the air a tension which was almost tangible.

This time it seemed, the unwritten rules of the game had been discarded and the seriousness of the situation enveloping him. Already he could sense that he might not be leaving for home in an hour or so. He thought again of his mother. The only anchor in his life. They both clung fiercely to one another in their struggle to survive. She would be sitting now, wondering what had happened this time. He wondered if the police had been in touch with her yet, and of the anguish she would be enduring if they had.

Lyons hunched over the table again. The booming voice caught Tommy off guard.

"Wherr's the knife son? Did ye fling it doon a drain like we heard?"

Tommy felt the chill as his already sweating body pressed against the cool robe.

"Wh...whit knife?"

Lyons stubbed his cigarette out in the cup and looked down the table. He seemed to stare at it for ages. He's hopin' I'll brekk the silence, thought Tommy. Nae chance. Incidents flickered across his mind again. Therr hud been a knife. But, wherr hud it come frae? Did ah use it? Lyons was staring at him now.

"Look son, whether ah win wi five clear goals, or it goes tae penalties, makes nae difference. Ah'm gettin' the two points, an you're gettin' relegated. Therr's nae other possible result. Why no' concede the match?"

"Look, look okay, ah hid a night oot. Drunk quite a bit, helluva lot actually. Ah canny mind much. There wis some kin' o' scuffle, Apart frae that, ah know nothin."

Lyons patted his shoulder.

"Calm doon son, ye're daein' fine. Jist think fur a minute or two. The rest o' it might come back tae ye."

Tommy's memory was like a pitch black room where the light would suddenly be switched on, then be put out again. Gradually, the still pictures began to merge into a film, but still with plenty of gaps. Granton Arms Drinking - BLANK - Sam's Bar disco - BLANK - more drink - BLANK - out in the street, raised voices - ANOTHER BLANK - the glint of a blade - ANOTHER BLANK. He rubbed his head as if trying to push the missing pieces into place.

Henderson came back into the room.

"Any word from the hospital, John?"

Henderson answered his colleague, but his face was turned toward Tommy.

"He'll be lucky tae see Monday mornin'."

Tommy jumped up, his chair tipping and falling on its back.

"Youse are bluffin'. It canny be that bad. Ah don't remember anythin' that bad happenin'. An...anyway, ah never hud a knife." The words came jerkily, sounding unconvincing.

"Lift the cherr an' sit back doon son." Tommy regained his seat. He longed for something to drink. His mouth was drying up, the lips sticky. He drew his tongue across them several times and swallowed.

"Awright, so therr wis a punch up. Whit else is new. But a know nothin' aboot a knife."

Henderson stood behind Tommy, leaning over just behind his head. Tommy could feel the spit touch his flesh as the man spoke into his ear.

"Ye know son, when ah wis your age, whit is it, twenty two? ah wisny interested in fightin'. Naw. When ah went tae the dancin' ma main aim wis tae try an shag somethin'."

"Oh aye. Lassies wis it?"

Henderson leant even closer. "When you're up in Barlinnie, ah think ye'll find the reality o' somebody's prick shoved up yer arse a lot less comical."

"John," Lyons cut in, "Nick oot an' get three coffees." Henderson straightened up and looked across the table. Lyons gestured with his head towards the door. Henderson looked again at Tommy and left.

"Smoke if ye like son." Lyons was speaking gently now. Tommy declined Lyons' cigarette, lighting one of his own.

"Ye know son, whit bothers me maist is the sheer waste o' human life. Therr's your life, hauf o' that's wasted noo. Then therr's the other boay. It looks as though his could be over. An' whit aboot yer maw? Aye, an' his tae. Dae ye think they'll get ower this easy?"

Tommy blew smoke upward to the ceiling.

"Look, let's get this straight. Therr wis a fight. It's comin' back to me noo. I'll tell ye aboot it."

Tommy ran the film through his head again. It was getting clearer all the time. He could see the picture of himself in the street...with a knife. He was stabbing stabb.......... he turned the film off.

"As ah wis sayin', therr wis a fight, but ah never hud a knife. If therr wis blood oan me, it wis probably because ah wis tryin' tae help or somethin'."

Lyons groaned.

"Oh aye, ye're in the Samaritans noo ah suppose?"

"Well, it must huv been somethin' like that. Ah must huv been close enough tae get splashed wi blood. Nae doot some o' ma pals will be able tae tell ye."

Lyons laughed. "Pals. PALS! They'll be the wans that telt us they saw you stab another boy repeatedly and then throw the knife doon a gratin' in the street." He's definitely bluffin thought Tommy. Naebody'd grass me.

Henderson returned with the drinks and Tommy fell silent, sucking nervously on his cigarette. A knock came at the door and a constable came in, handed a package to Henderson, whispered something in his ear and went out again. Henderson and Lyons were talking but Tommy couldn't make out what they were saying. Lyons threw the package on the table. Through the clear plastic , Tommy saw it. It looked harmless now, away from danger, but still stained. The pictures still missing began to fall into place in the film running through Tommy's mind again.

There had been no real reason for it. Just too many bottles that contained not only alcohol but naked aggression as well. As Jekyll changed to Hyde, Tommy enjoyed the sensation of power in watching the fear in others. The trembling limbs and ashen faces fuelled his fire. He could be the master.....for a while. The final picture slotted into its frame. "Stick 'im Tommy. Stick 'im!" A knife appeared and Tommy gripped it. The crowd roared him on. "Plunge the bastard. Let 'im huv it."

A wave of hysteria had carried him the rest of the way. Lyons held the knife in front of Tommy's face.

"Recognise it son?" Tommy didn't speak. "Ye don't need tae speak, yer eyes tell everything."

The door knocked and a uniformed sergeant stuck his head through the opening.

"Excuse me Derek. You're wanted. Urgent." Lyons turned to Henderson.

"Get it on paper John. I'll be back." Once outside he addressed the sergeant. "If it's about the prints being washed away from the knife, forget it. He's about to make a confession." The sergeant stared intently at Lyons.

"No, it's not that."

Tommy was sitting quietly, drinking tea, when Lyons returned. He seemed totally subdued. Henderson had several sheets of foolscap paper in front of him. He lifted one of them and showed Lyons Tommy's signature at the foot of the page. Lyons nodded. He remained standing.

"Ever heard of a David Burns son?" Tommy shook his head.

"Sure? Want to think again?"

Tommy stared at the ceiling. It was some time before he answered.

"Only David Burns I ever knew wis a cousin o' mine. Huvny seen 'im fur aboot ten years. Ah think ma mother an' his still see wan another sometimes. Ah widny know 'im if he walked through that door."

Lyons sighed deeply.

"Oh, he won't be walkin' through any doors. Except maybe the pearly gates. Tommy's face registered first puzzlement, then disbelief and, finally, horror. His jaw moved but no words came. The eyes twitched, then rolled and Lyons had to rush to catch the body as it crumpled to the floor.

It was three forty-five. Sunday afternoon. A constable went to Tommy's cell to collect the plate which he had left earlier. As he expected, it was untouched, the food congealed, glued to the plate. Tommy lay, curled in the foetal position, crying into his pillow. The sobbing continued into the night.

In Drumchapel and Rutherglen the sound of tormented, grieving women also continued into the night.....and well beyond.

Peter Arthur

Dreams of a Small Dog

Pepe goes for walkies,
travels local streets,
barks at folk he meets,
yaps, snaps, craps,
and having done these things,
goes home, lies down, sleeps
and dreams a doggie dream.

Pepe dreams of Mexico; canine compadres,
Sierra Madres, village padres,
caballeros, mescaleros
commancheros and other pistoleros.
In his dreams he'll meet some sweet chiquitta
named Margarita or Lolita,
go Acapulco, maybe fandango in Durango,
smoke some marijuana in Tijuana
and then, *Hasta Manyana*
until he dreams again.

Sometimes, when Pepe has a snooze
he dreams he's down in Veracruz
or dreams of being a stray in Monterrey
and who can blame him? Scotland's no place
for a Chihuahua.

Vampires

Vampires have a nasty disposition
due to having undergone transition
from life to limbo,
permanently suffering
spiritual travel sickness.
Deprived of their eternal rest,
and having passed the coffin test,
they're driven forth
to sate a blood desire.
Vampires need veins
to ease the pains
of their remains,
a walking miasma
devoid of cells and plasma.
Mortality denied,
they haven't died.
They're just
undead
instead.

Straight Jacket Racket

Shrieking kids surround me.
Next door, a stereo explodes
through 40 watt speakers,
its Sonic shrapnel pierces my skull.
Dogs bark incessantly
and aggravate my wounds.
White noise would be soothing muzak
compared to these tortuous decibels.
My nerves, stretched like taut twine,
snap with a quiet twang,
which goes unnoticed
in this overflowing dustbin of din.

Air Drop

A child holds out its hands for food,
though more than starving, it does no good.
Little black hands, swollen stomach, thin face,
inspires pity, or, horror (of another race?)
Overhead, mean rain-clouds pass,
ignoring lonely clumps of grass.
Oblivious to peoples' pain,
Blue white sky keeps its rain.

A natural disaster, drought,
nothing much to shout about.
So many, so hungry, well, so what!
Not our fault, a famine onslaught.
A civil war competes with thirst
to see who gets a victim first.
Unworthy conflict in a land
somewhere in Africa, with sand.

Nation with a name obscure,
how much more can you endure?
stalked by so many predators
and much more savage creditors.

Your wars and hunger have no end,
on richer peoples you depend.
We have food, mountains high,
we will drop some from the sky.

For every ounce of food, a bullet flies,
for each life saved, another dies.
Balance of nature, or, balance of books?
wars have their advocates, and crooks.

Rosina Gilmour

Windows ...

Windows,
    arched
    round
    oval
    square
Windows
    dirty
    frosted
    tinted
    clear
Windows
    broken
    boarded
    barred
    sequered
Windows
    decorated
    neglected
    pretentious
    poor

Windows on walls
set in cold stone
deliberately

Windows on walls
breaking the barriers
boldly

Windows on walls
parting the brick
religiously

Windows on walls
reflecting the light
warmly

"WINDOW...an opening in the wall of a building to let in air and light."

WINDOWS ABANDONED ...

Shattered window, staring from stone,
sometimes the fragments glitter in the
fading light,
while slivers of glass drop like tears.
Sorrowful sight.

Broken window, battered by stone,
once bright and beloved feature
bare now,
betrayed by the very thing that held you,
being brave.

THE INSCRIPTION

John Farrel arose from a restless night's sleep, to a stark November morning peering steel-grey, through the half drawn bedroom curtains. He glanced with feigned indifference at the clock, picked up the dressing gown which littered the bed-end, and forgot to put on his slippers. As he descended the steep staircase, the creaking wood groaned in sympathy with his aching form, but with a final moan the flight was negotiated successfully and he breathed a sigh of relief.

When his feet made contact with the stone-clad kitchen floor, an involuntary shiver ran through his being. Staring at the bareness of his feet, his thoughts became oddly preoccupied. His mind was focused beyond the image, and what he saw was a small reflection of the demise of his meticulously planned life-style. From rising to settling, and every hour in between, his time like other commodities, such as money and intellect, were thoroughly harnessed and used efficiently. Hunger eventually recalled him to the present.

Tea made, the process conducted almost reverently, he made the decision to take breakfast in the sitting room. This was no mere impulse of course, in truth he ached too much to climb back upstairs to retrieve the forgotten slippers, and so the sheer discomfort of the cold underfoot persuaded him that the task of managing the breakfast tray along a short corridor was by far the wisest solution to an uncomfortable situation.

The sitting room possessed an air of emptiness, although lumbering furniture, deeply stained, sober and practical, occupied its area carefully. A room reflecting its owner's taste and affluence, and perhaps his character. Although not a rich man, John Farrel, Solicitor and Notary Public, had (as he had often been heard to state), through diligence and thrift, acquired a perfectly comfortable existence.

He liked this room. It had become, over the years, his retreat from the demanding pressures of business. Sometimes in the evenings he would peruse the bookcase, and settle in his favourite chair to read, or on occasions, he would listen to music. He once surprised himself by allowing a feeling of deep contentment to overcome him, and inspire thoughts that perhaps the dark recesses and subdued atmosphere of the room stirred in his subconscious, and evoked memories of womb-like peace.

However, emotions springing from fanciful thoughts were quickly suppressed, for he concluded years ago that ideas of this nature were best expressed by the feminine character, to whom they more naturally belonged.

This morning he noticed the room had become less inviting in the insipid morning light, its dusty corners and true colours exposed by the unflattering hue. Breakfast over, the unfaltering beat of the mantle clock now commanded his attention, its orderly face issuing the unspoken command that time must be considered. A pang of anxiety gripped him, and trying to blanket the emotion with reason, he got up and walked uneasily to the bookcase. Some semblance of routine would quell this rising tide of emotion, he felt convinced of that, and muttered the words to himself, as a mother would whisper reassurance to a frightened child perhaps listening to the shriek of a dentist's drill from the suffocating stillness of the waiting room.

His gaze fell upon a sepia photograph, well-protected by ornate wooden frame and flawless glass. His mother had not been generous with her endearments. He recalled her prescriptive statements for coping with any unpleasantness life presented. He found no solace then in her uncompromising words - "One must face one's fate bravely John, like a man." Her colourless image still haunted him. He had tried desperately to please her, to be the man, since that cataclysmic evening, when he was eight. Father disappeared from life. Mother wept sincerely on his young and fragile shoulders.

From then on, she ran her household and personal life with military precision, void of sentiment to the bitter end. She loved her son, but from a distance, and her ultimate ambition was to see him succeed. It would be her salvation in a society where marital failure demoted one to the ranks of the unprincipled. She had been selfish, a woman scorned, but she had been loyal to her cause. He turned from the memory and his fingers trembled as they scanned the books. They were well-worn and well read. His hands finally came to rest on a soft hide-bound volume, which he did not instantly recognize. It bore a faint, musty smell, and dog-eared pages protruded from the faded leather.

"Poetry" he murmured, and thought it strangely misplaced among the venerable classics. He had not noticed it before, indeed, mother had discouraged his fondness for this art. As a young Freshman, he recalled her frosty reception when he presented her with a verse he had painstakingly contrived for her, on his return from the first semester. He had missed her, and had hoped earnestly that their separation might result in a demonstrative welcome. Fired by this hope and unsuppressed by the atmosphere of home, he courageously embraced her and thrust the precious parchment into her hands, along with a tidy posy of forget-me-nots.

Her response had been curt. Whatever true emotions lay beneath the brittle veneer of her character remained there unexpressed.

"You really must disengage yourself from frivolous emotion John, if you are going to succeed. Sentimental ramblings will not secure you a respectable position in life."

Silence had ensued, and the incident overshadowed the following weeks, until, with a mixture of both guilt and relief, he returned to his studies, trying as best he could to obey, avoiding the aesthetic, not just to please her but to disassociate himself with the memory of that unpleasant day.

He shuffled back to his chair and eased himself into it. A long forgotten sense of pleasure lifted his spirits as he studied the book. KEATS, the simple title contrasted sharply with the ornate gold of the lettering. The deep saffron leather had mellowed with age, grown sallow and soft to touch, almost flesh- like, and he felt comforted by the texture, as if clasping a firm but gentle hand. He opened the book at the beginning, his orderly mind unable to release itself from years of conformity, and allow him the simple pleasure of selecting at random a word or verse that might uplift and inspire, and wantonly fulfill the need of the moment.

Immediately, his attention was drawn to a short inscription, the faded ink and graceful writing adorning an otherwise blank page. *'Dum vivamus, vivimus'* -

While we live, let us live, The Latin was precise. As if frozen by the breath of winter itself, John Farrel's body chilled. He paled as the fragile peace between himself and his predicament shattered. Memories of a time deliberately forgotten, now paraded themselves unashamedly before him, and that fate could have chosen such a moment to unearth this evidence from the past seemed almost unjust. Time, it seemed, had not absolved him of his shame, but self-denial had allowed him to live with it.

The book, a parting gift, had been given with love and sadness to a young graduate, eager to challenge the world and conquer injustice. How bright those memories now burned, as forty years of living dissolved and he remembered the vigour of youth strengthen his resolve. His enthusiasm for loving had blossomed unfettered by the confines of home, and for that brief period his spirits soared to lofty heights, as later his career had done, though only through sacrifice, his true aspirations left on the altar of conformity.

His eyes clouded, as they had on that fateful morning, when he made the choice which set his destiny. If indeed there had been a choice for John Farrel. He had no faith in love, not even one as deep as theirs. Neither family nor society would have accepted it, and mother - the disgrace would have destroyed her. In the end, reason swayed his decision, that impassionate voice that presents a noble and feasible argument, shunning emotion and swaying the faint-hearted. He found himself not guilty, providing there was total estrangement.

John Farrel closed his eyes, as he had closed his mind to the situation so many years before. Perhaps, he thought, if he had inherited more of his father's flair for living, the determination and single-mindedness which had led him ultimately beyond the perimeters of respectability, he too could have been strong enough to crush the barriers of self-deceit and delusion which constrained him, but he had never found that courage. He envied his father, at least the picture he had formed of the man with the ambiguous nature, from snippets of information he had gleaned over the years. It was not his aesthetic gifts or sensitivity he coveted, it was the notion that he had faded into obscurity, with no more regrets than any other man, and no less graced with his share of happiness. Being true to oneself, it seemed, brought its own bittersweet rewards, a great deal more satisfying than the bland fruits his own life had produced.

The eleventh hour was struck by the clock, and jolted John Farrel back to the imminent. He picked up the telephone by his chair, and nervously dialled six digits. A voice that instantly reminded him of his mother affected politeness, stated the name of the practice and invited conversation. He tried as best he could to express himself, through the dense plastic and jangled nerves. The reply was cool - "Yes Mr Farrel, Doctor Chambers would like to see you tomorrow at 2pm, if that's convenient... it is?... fine... and do try to be punctual, thank you." A polite exchange of goodbyes were offered, and he replaced the receiver. The worst was over and he could now resign himself to the reality of the facts. If the first tests had offered some dubiety, the second had obviously proved conclusive and Dr Chambers had prepared him for it, mentioned various treatments, the possibility of three to five years.

John Farrel reclined in his chair. He felt aged and worn, but somehow at peace with himself. Clutching the musty anthology, he glanced once more at the inscription - *'While we live, let us live'* - and he knew the giver had done just that. Lived life to its fullest, without compromise and without him. Although denied the comfort of family and homeland, had been free to be himself and to find those things which truly gave life joy and meaning. His voice quavered and he found himself uttering a solemn vow, to the memory of a love he had not had the heart to hold. He would live life to its fullest, whatever there was left of it, truthfully and with courage, and in a final gesture of submission to self-truth, he drew his hand tenderly across the face of the book and whispered a name, once spoken with such love - "Dearest Philip, please forgive me..."

Alex Potts

"Wu'll No Be Long"

Ma Ma in Da ur gone oot
a kin see thir gettin ready
ma Da's shavin hair aff his face
in am quite good it that inawe
cos a practice oan ma teddy

She puts oan hunners a perfume
in hunners a lipstick
oh a hate when ma Ma's gettin done up
Well a don't mind really, but it shouldny be so thick
cos before she goes oot she his her tea
in it leaves a big red mooth oan her cup
in it nearly makes me sick

That lassie fae roon the corner's watchin me
ma Ma gies her money fir it
but she always brings her boyfriend
in a sneak in in watch theam kiss
in she nearly his a fit

She's pretty daft that lassie
a kin get anythin a ask
awe a hiv tae dae is lie oan the carpet in greet
then she ignores me in a greet harder
then she comes up way it fast

When ma Ma in Da come in am suppost tae be asleep
but a listen in hear thim say 'How wis the wean'?
'Oh the wean wis great' is always the reply
noo a know whit the big yins mean
when they say a wee white lie.

The Release Of Thoughts From The Brain Using Others As A Stimulus..... *Title Under Review*

Compel me to scribe a point of ink to the virgin paper
Compel me to let flood the sleeping lake of sweat through
My arid, workshy skin
Compel a thought of my own not formed from the thinking of another
Compel me to think that I am not what I appear to myself
But to other people
Compel me to these things for I shall not accomplish them alone
A giant of sloth and laziness dwells within my body
One which rules supreme
No knight am I to slay this monster
Aid from outside to rekindle my heroism
To vanquish the obscenity from this place called Me
Is what I need and crave
A champion of fluid thought and ideas which wreak havoc
On half-formed notions and let the light of lucidity
Take over from the darkness of dithering
I am imprisoned in my own world, my cell is made from
Great Blocks of mental which I claw at in the vain hope
Of freedom, my dreams keep me sane
Liberation of my thoughts to attain, to let others
Drink from my mental stream to quaff fully of my ideas
And to let them live on, my soul bared and satisfied.

Mr Inside

You're never alone with yourself
The talk is always relative to your own interests
The arguments within never spill over to the outside
You're a calm and reasonable and intelligent talker
It appears as though you are the one with the ideas
Who do they think said it first anyway?
Not everyone can think like you
You laugh inside, idiots!
They don't know who they're dealing with
I could show them, if I wanted.
But not yet not yet
It'll keep.

CHRISTINE STEWART

GROWING OLD

I look into the mirror and what did I see?
Two baggy eyes staring back at me
I took a closer look and got the fright of my life
I'm growing a beard and I'm the bloody wife
The face that once was pretty and thin
Now adorns a double chin
Alas I cannot tell a lie
The blonde hair on my head's a dye
I must admit my figure's not too bad
A few stretch marks I once never had
My boobs have dropped an inch or two
I'm getting old - what can I do
If I stand back a few feet from the mirror
I can see my whole body shake and shimmer
I suppose it's something we have to accept
I mean I'm thirty three what do you expect....

G.L. BUGLASS

SCRAMBLED EGGS

Yellow white in mottled store,
Or case unspeckled round the core;
To crackle in the frying pan,
And be delivered in a van;
Or lightly poached within a pot,
Or boiled in water piping hot.

Beaten to a frothy foam,
Or like the Taj-mahal, a dome;
Lightly switched to dizzy heights,
Or painted faces Easter sights;
In some delicate cuisine,
Crumbling like a Pharaoh's scene.

Arrayed the guards bareheaded stand,
Or spongy mass with a band;
Snowy peaks in frozen wastes,
Plays with anthem to the tastes;
Seed of Life outside the Womb,
Companion in a lonely room.

Eileen Hart

Body Language

He turned the bathroom tap on and watched the clear cool liquid as it flowed and swirled through his hands. Cupping them together he gathered some and splashed his face in an attempt to waken himself up, pull himself into the day that stretched ahead. He looked into the mirror on the bathroom cabinet. What a sight. His eyes were red rimmed, his complexion sallow, he needed a shave, badly. The man in the mirror had had too many late nights, sleepless, boozing. Get a grip Frank. Get a grip, he said to himself. The day he'd dreaded had finally dawned, and he was relieved to face it.

The bitch had wanted it, longed for it. For his part he had obliged her. Secret come-ons she'd given, no one else had picked them up, but he had. But then he'd always been quick on the uptake when it came to females. He knew how sexy and attractive he was to them. Oh, but the way she tossed her head, tongue wetting her lips, looking at him. He'd watched her, sitting, legs crossed, moving her hand up and down them, slowly, tauntingly. He never doubted signals. The way she glided by him, wiggling her hips. And the perfume: overpowering, wafting around him as she passed his desk in the office. And what a body. She reminded him of a Sindy doll.

Well a man's gotta do what a man's gotta do was his philosophy, so he'd decided to make some moves of his own. He'd brushed by her unnecessarily close on every occasion, made excuses to approach her desk, talk to her. Made sure his eyes swept up and down her body, longingly. Covering her hand with his as she passed any paperwork to him. He knew she was loving it. Especially the odd nip in the bum.

Sure even in the canteen hadn't she looked at him as he queued for his lunch? Frank knew what she wanted. He obliged. Wasn't he well known as being an obliging bloke? So he sat beside her. Squeezed his leg against hers. She didn't move away. He noticed she'd left her lunch untouched. Obviously the gal was too busy fighting back her overwhelming desires.

He finished shaving and patted on some aftershave. He felt better. He'd get a good night's sleep tonight, after his celebratory drink with the boys. As he closed his front door behind him he thought about the ridiculous charge he was going to face. Sexual harassment in the workplace. What a joke! If anyone had been sexually harassed it had been him. Females, couldn't keep their mitts off him. He whistled as he walked down the road. Feeling confident. She had been like all the rest. A tease. But no one else had ever complained. They had all played along, enjoying every minute of it. Till they moved on to another job. Yeah, moved on to another job. He stopped in his tracks, his whistling tailed off to be lost in the noise and hubbub of the busy street.

DAVID PEARCE

THE JOURNEY BACK

Through a window of rain-streaked dirt
I study the horizon. The city
at sunrise is restless
tired of the constant flow.

Streams of belching buses hold
a cargo of unfamiliar faces while
workers drive impatient,
full of priorities.

I step down to the platform
to be swept with the tide
pushed and jostled out to the street
a street filled with businessmen and beggars
reminding me of the divide
between the have and have nots.

In my absence new buildings have sprung
from aged decrepit remains:
a sand-blasted town now,
not the weary image I'd known.
It welcomes me back.
I've come home.

Echoes

Chromed and perfected taps
drip echoes of an empty house
reflecting shadowless walls
playing children remembered on
a broken-backed horse.

Stairs uncrept creak to the sound
of the rusty-hinged gate
no footsteps, no slow key turns
no shouts or welcomes at the door
just paper on the dusty floor.

Branches of a naked tree scratch
against the moonlit pane of glass
sleepless nights spent gazing out
across rolling fields, long ago
taps still drip in an empty house.

Margaret Millmaker

The Waiting Game

The baby safe in the embryo sac, waiting to be born,
The toddler waiting for Santa to give him his present
at the playgroup party.
The schoolchild waiting for his school exam results,
The youth waiting for a reply from a job interview,
The teenage boy waiting for his Girocheque,
The teenage girl waiting for results of a pregnancy test,
The young mother waiting for a Council house,
The Father waiting to see how many will be made redundant,
The Mother waiting for the teenager to come home,
The Granny waiting for the results of a biopsy,
The Grandfather waiting to die,
The whole world waiting.

Mary

She loved,
She gave,
Just like a slave.

He used,
Abused,
Led her to an early grave.

The people came to say goodbye,
He came too ...
I wonder why.

Private War

Look at me, I am small,
You are strong, and you are tall.

Look at me, they've shaved my head,
I lie all day in a sodden bed.

Look at me, I can't smile,
I've been here for quite a while.

Look at me. Caucescu child,
Imprisoned here, not running wild.

Look at me don't pass me by,
I can't laugh, and I don't cry.

Look at me, look at me
Can you find a home for me?

Look at me, no don't shed tears,
I'll be here for many years.

COLETTE COEN

OIL

She is never sure of what to wear on these ritual trips to the airport. Should she be in her finery - dressed as though on a date, feeling all the anxiety that accompanies it? Or should she feign a casualness she should by now feel? She knows that he'll be there in jeans or sweatpants, but there's still a temptation to impress him, and make him feel good about coming home to her.

Today, she showers then dresses in her new casual clothes, dabs on Chanel and some lipstick, then lingers for a while, tidying up the mess of the day: washing the one plate, hiding her singleness.

At the airport she is caught up in the mass anticipation, lettting the excitement seep into her. Everyone is getting high on travel, and the thrill of the unknown.

He ruins her wait by being first off the plane, and she feels almost cheated out of these last few precious moments of hope. But she can't stop herself from smiling, and rushing towards him, holding him tightly to her:

"Oh Matthew."

He kisses her lightly on the lips and releases himself from this embarrassing public display which no one has noticed.

"Hiya, darling, how you doing?"

She's been six weeks without him, how can she begin to explain how she's been doing, so she just smiles and takes his hand, and says;

"Fine."

In the car park, before he can ask his usual question, Louise hands him the keys. He opens the door for her, and as she tries to do her seatbelt from the opposite side, he puts his bags in the boot. A minute later he's pushing back the driver's seat, and adjusting the mirror. Louise watches him in silence.

On the way home Matthew talks about his trip; about the weather, the laddish exploits, the food and the trips onshore. Louise listens, watching the road more carefully than Matthew, moving her feet in time with his manoeuvres.

Back in the flat there is little time for conversation as Matthew dumps his bags at the door and leads Louise to bed.

As he sleeps she clings to him, ashamed that she should cling to any man; trying desperately to disguise from them both how much she clings; how she has made him an anchor in her Sea of Despond. He would recoil if he knew how she clung to him as he slept, and give an irritated laugh if he knew the reason. He knew he was still alive during each of the forty-two days he had been away; he knew he was coming back. So Louise, unable to hear his contempt, and quiet anger at being thought vulnerable, and mortal, no longer told him of her anxieties. But she still worried when he was away, worried every moment of every day. She worried that her fortnightly phonecall would not come, and that the other unexpected phonecall, which she constantly dreaded, would :

"I'm afraid there's been an accident."

So she clung to him, clung whenever she could.

Her life was always so different when he was home: so free from these concerns, but also free from the accompanying hope. She didn't even watch the news when he was onshore. It held no morbid fascination for her now. It was for others to watch and wait for the next crash, the next fire, the next avoidable, unavoidable accident.

Matthew twitches his limbs into a deeper sleep, and turns from Louise, his legs beating out the message as he goes that he is safe and sound. It is not so easy for Louise to sleep. In one way she loves these quiet moments when she can refill her memory with silent images of him, and just rejoice in the pleasure of his presence. Yet in another way she almost resents the intrusion. As she drifts off to sleep she often wakens, sensing a breath that is not hers, or a movement or sound she did not make; and she has to remind herself that tonight, at least, her husband shares her marital bed.

Louise wakes early and sneaks from the bed without disturbing Matthew. She makes a coffee and unpacks his bags, throwing the washing into the machine as she goes. There's more perfume in a duty- free bag: he used to say that he was stocking up for when he stopped this offshore work, but now he doesn't even make a present out of it. It is merely there in amongst the dirty underwear. The post arrives and Louise opens everything regardless of whom it is addressed to.

At half past ten the phone rings. Matthew's mum, phoning for her weekly chat with Louise. For a moment Louise is tempted to keep Matthew's return a secret, knowing too well that if she tells, she'll have to share him. But Matthew has been disturbed by the noise and stumbles into the hall.

"He's here, actually, I'll just put him on".
Then to Matthew:
"It's your mum."
Louise returns to the kitchen to re-boil the kettle and tries not to listen:
"Of course we'll come tomorrow. No we can't today. I think I'll be going to the football."
Louise slams down a mug, hoping that Matthew can hear, but angry at herself for being so surprised: what was more important than a Saturday on the terraces, a day with your mother, or with your wife?
She tries not to sound accusatory when Matthew comes in looking for his breakfast:
"Are you really going to the football today, Matthew?"
He comes beside her, putting his arms around her waist, trying to be irresistible:
"Well, yes, I was hoping to. They're playing at home this week, I'll not be away too long."
"No, just the whole afternoon. How do you know they're at home anyway?"
"Ah, well the World Service is a wonderful thing you know."
Louise pulls away from him:
"Yeah, wonderful."
"Why don't you go round the shops and buy yourself something nice?"
"I don't feel like being bought off today, thanks all the same, and I'm fed up spending every Saturday going round the shops looking for nice things to buy, just for the sake of spending money."

Louise stops herself short, hardly understanding why she is antagonising the man she loves. She goes over and planks herself on his knee, gently caressing his neck:
"I just want to spend some time with you, is that so terrible?"
But she has gone too far, and he has spent too much time in chauvinistic company to be brought around with such sweet-talk:
"Yeah, that would be great fun in the mood you're in."
Retreating back to her own chair, Louise decides that she might as well have a big fight now, as lots of small ones later:
"What did your mum say?"
"I said we would go there tomorrow for dinner."
"That's strange," says Louise, punctuating her sentence with a sip of coffee:
"I said the exact same thing to my mum yesterday."

"Shit, Louise, I hardly see my mum. She wants me there tomorrow, that's where I'm going to be. OK? I'm going for a shower."

She tries not to cry as she clears the breakfast dishes, then goes to phone her mum:

"Hi,...Yeah. Listen, Matthew's back, and, well, he kind of wants to see his mum tomorrow, is it OK if we come over next week instead? I'm really sorry, you know what it's like, I'll phone during the week, OK?"

After that call she phones and cancels her plans for the girls' night out. The same excuse, always the same excuse for rearranging her life, and the lives of those around her: "Matthew's back." She knows her friends must be getting tired of all this, as she knows she is tired of all these excuses. Matthew would tell her not to change her plans on his account, but one of them had to make sacrifices if they were ever going to see each other.

When he gets back from the football, three hours after the final whistle, Louise is all ready for a night on the town. Matthew knows better than to argue with this tradition, and although he no longer chooses and books the restaurant, he is back in time to get ready for the meal. It was on these occasions that Louise could have her say: but first, all the news. A lot happens in six weeks, more than can possibly be squeezed into a few hours. So Louise fills him in on only the major happenings in the Western World, and in her life. But like any news bulletin, there is only two minutes left at the end for human interest, and by this time Matthew has already switched off and is calling for the bill.

Louise wonders if Matthew even notices the strain their separation has put on her. She hates that she can no longer be the fun-loving person she was during their courtship, but that was before the sea captured him again. Periodially she asks about normal work: the kind he always used to promise would be found soon; the kind that is dull, and badly paid, and means you have to live at home, live with your wife; the kind that means you have responsibilities; the kind that doesn't take you to an all-male preserve.

As they walk home together Louise lets the wine, and the pleasure of being with Matthew, calm her troubled mind. For a couple of hours she can at least recapture some of the happiness she used to feel before she knew of the sea and her desires; before she could see the darkness at the end of every tunnel of light; before she felt the hand, always ready to snatch him away.

Louise is called to the phone on Tuesday morning:

"I think it's your husband."

Louise hears something about Bill not being able to make the next trip, and Matthew being the only one available who can do the job. She swallows hard, not wanting to hear any more:

"I'll have to leave today."

"What? What time?"

"Half twelve. I've got to be at the airport in an hour."

Louise knows that there is no way she can make it home in time, and doesn't really feel like another emotional good-bye, so they talk practicalities, and Louise forgets to tell Matthew that she loves him. When he hangs up the phone, Louise runs to the loo and throws up.

During an afternoon meeting, as one of her colleagues drones on, Louise passes out. When she comes round, she makes excuses about the heat, and her period, and refuses to go back home to her empty flat. She knows that the pregnancy rumours are already flying after the morning's exploits, but there is nothing she can say to dispel them. The women she works with love the idea of a part-time husband, and often tease her about her great life. They are jealous of the casual wealth Louise is acquiring, the wealth she cares nothing for. She wants only one thing: a normal life. A life where arrangements can be made and kept; where concert tickets can be bought with no thought of contingency plans. She wants a life where she can fall asleep next to her husband every night, and wake up knowing that he is there in the morning.

For the rest of the day, and for the weeks ahead, Louise mixes her worries with the thought of escape from them. "Maybe one day he'll come back and I'll not be waiting, and maybe he'll worry where I am, and whether I'm safe. And maybe one day he'll understand my worries, and feel how I feel every minute of every day. And maybe, just maybe, I'll not come back."

THOMAS ANDERSON

THE SMUGGLERS' ARMS

This dim but lively place is called the Smugglers' Arms .
The crew that's holding court, have all the tricks and charms.
While the buzzard holds the key, there's nothing left to chance.
His crew and all before him, will be led a merry dance.

In through the door blows the snatch, the dip and kite,
To share the spoils of the day, you've never seen the like.
A few swift moves a hasty break, they've settled for the night
And in their wake the losers trail, in wonder of the flight.

The buzzard's in the corner, his perch against the wall
Waiting for the first to slip, so he can have it all,
While the teller of the tale sits within his world of charm,
Runs his pen across the page inside the Smuggler's Arms.

The Inn is looking good tonight, the snatch is feeling mean
The Kite has found another score, the Buzzard picks him clean
As they sail out of the fray, they're headed for the Bar.
Let's have a drink for this crew, we're thirsty for a jar.

The silver hits the table, "Landlord serve another drink."
He turns his back, the dope is passed, before he'd time to think.
The crew have split the booty. Tonight the race is on
The dip has hit another sucker. The day is still not done.

As the Buzzard and his crew, leave the Inn that night
A trick they dipped lay in wait, so he could set things right.
With a double barrel shotgun, and murder on his mind
He gave both barrels of that gauge to the Buzzard and the Kite.

From the street a cry was heard, the law are on the scene
Too late. The trick made haste. He faded like a dream
Both bodies felled by the gun, are left to rot and die
Now the Buzzard and the Kite, will roam the midnight sky.

The Snatch and the Dip now own the perch against the wall
They slipped the plan that was laid and now have got it all,
While the teller of the tale, sits within his world of charm
And brings this story to a close, inside The Smuggler's Arms.

Austin Docherty

In My Room

In my room there are two doors.
One, the way to fredom and life,
the other, a dead-end.
My wardrobe with all my clothes
and belongings.
Everything I ever owned
has been in that wardrobe.
In my room there is me.
I am on the television and
in the bed, in the bike and
on the clock.
In my room the midi system is mine
but I belong to it.
I don't know what I would do
if I lost my sound system.
In my room my life's photographs
are on the door in the corner,
The door lets a draught in
and sometimes, a photograph falls.

Highrise

A twenty storey building
wae two hundred different flats
his granny's oan the bottom
an a lift right tae the tap

The graffiti covered wa's
say 'UP THE IRA' and 'THE POLIS TAE'
and they tell ye a the things
that oor young Karen can dae.

But for young mum Mary
who lives oan the tap flair
the best bit's when
the lifts are oot and so is the milk
and her boy's away
tae get some mair.

ALEX TELFORD

LIVING BOOK

The classroom stirred as the final few minutes of the day approached. There began the increasing rustle of books being closed and bags being opened signifying the impatient desire of the pupils to be free of the place. Mr Dick, the history teacher, caught their attention by positioning himself between them and the classroom door. With a sly grin he delivered a devastating blow to the class of reluctant listeners.

"As your first history assignment of this term, you will compile a project. Working in pairs, I would like you all to research the people, places, events and dates of importance during World War II. That's all, thank you!"

"Sir! We know that we won. Is that no' enough?" asked Diane McAuslan from beneath the desk where she was hastily throwing books into her shoulder bag.

"I'm not merely interested in the result Diane, I want to know who was invaded, where things happened and how the game was played".

"Here, is this the World War or the World Cup we're talking about?"

"Oh, very good, but if we won then it certainly wasn't the World Cup!"

"Aye true." Diane was enjoying this banter when she noticed her friend Angela waiting in the doorway.

"Jist comin."

Diane and Angela trod their twice daily route home through the woodpaths and shops in the easy silence that comes from almost total companionship; comfortable with their own thoughts and a broken conversation that neither of them felt any pressure to keep flowing. As they reached Diane's close, their attention turned to what they would do that night. Angela looked at Diane and arched her eyebrows, waiting for a suggestion.

"D'ye fancy goin' to the library for a while to see if we can find some books fur our war project?"

Angela forced a smile.

"Aye, a'right, but the excitement might kill me! See you later."

On her way home Angela nipped into the wee grocer's shop below her house. She took out the note her mum had left her that morning and bought the few things listed for that night's supper. This had become almost routine since her mum had taken full-time work after Angela's dad was made redundant.

Closing the front door with the back of her heel she called out to her dad that she was home and put the message bags in the kitchen. Going into the living room, Angela went towards her dad who sat apparently watching T.V.

"What ye watching?" she asked, leaning over the back of his chair.

"Eh! Och I wisnae really watching it, jist sort of staring at the screen. D'ye know what a mean, wee yin?"

Angela looked at him for a minute. She noticed that his hair was beginning to grey at the side. He sat leaning to one side in the chair, with his legs crossed very tightly. His foot tapped incessantly. In one hand a lit cigarette burned away unsmoked as he chewed away at the fingernails of his other hand. As Angela looked at her dad she wanted to touch him but he looked so tense that she couldn't be sure how he would react. Instead she moved about, tidying here and there, trying to chat with him.

"Did ye go anywhere t'day da?"

"No, I didnae bother. I was thinking about goin' to the Job Centre but I was there yesterday so I didnae bother."

"Was that no' two days ago?"

"No, it couldnae've been, wee yin," he answered, shifting position slightly.

Moving back through to the kitchen to unpack the shopping, she felt a little bit sad. As she put the kettle on for some tea, Angela thought about how much she had come to enjoy her dad being home when she came in from school. When he was first out of work he was not always there, but after a while it had become so regular that she expected it. She had enjoyed the chance to talk and just share the house with each other before everyone else came home. Recently though, this had just become a hollow passing of time before supper and the inevitable arguments that would come.

Just before six that evening, Angela set out for Diane's. As she walked up the hill, saying "hello" to almost exactly the same people she did most nights, she thought, half to herself and half out loud,

"I wunner how many times I've walked up this bit of road to meet her? Must t'morra be thousands, t'morra she can come up for me!"

As she said this she knew it wouldn't happen. Angela's going to Diane's was one of the unmentioned but established ways in which their friendship worked and remained comfortable. In fact it was almost without thinking that after supper she would go to Diane's house then on to whatever action that night held. Tonight it was going to the local library to study. Angela almost puked at the thought! She had enough of books in school and the thought of spending the evening surrounded by ones about the second World War, was almost as bad as staying in with her Ma and Da.

Reaching out and opening the door to the McAuslan's house, Angela poked her head around and called out,

"Hi, it's only me."

Above the sound of dishes being washed came the voice of Diane's dad from the kitchen.

"Hello there, she's in her room, go on through."

On the way down the hall, Angela stopped to check herself in the mirror and grimaced at the limp appearance of her hair, which was straight and pulled back in a pony. Not very appealing, she thought, but at least it looked better than it did when it was hanging down.

"Hiya!" she said.

Diane stood amongst a pile of clothes wearing only her underwear and a black top.

"O'hiya. I cannae find ma white denims, its daein ma head in so it is."

Angela settled down for what she knew could be quite a wait.

"Put something else on then. We're only goin' tae the library."

"Aye, but you never know who might be there Angie" replied Diane from inside a cupboard.

"Oh, that's right. Marti Pellow usually comes doon with his books on a Thursday. I forgot that."

"Shut up you!"

Picking a tape off the floor, Angela put it on.

"Remember the library shuts at eight."

"Have you all got tickets?" Okay, no tickets, then out!"

Approaching the counter, Angela caught Diane's arm.

"We'll just look for some books ourself. When you ask for help, one of them usually walks about asking questions in a loud voice and everybody hears whit yere looking for; its embarrassing so it is."

They worked their way through the books trying to find a place to begin taking notes, but after a fair bit of study all they had was:

- 3rd September 1939:- Britain declares war after German invasion of Poland. Hitler's Germany against the United Forces of Britain, France and Russia.
- 1941:- America enters war after bombing of Pearl Harbour by Japanese.
- 1945:- War ends.

Diane thumped her book shut.

"This is useless. How are we supposed to make something interesting out of this boring old crap?"

Angela gave her a long-suffering look.

"Whit dae ye expect? It's history in'it - it's supposed tay be boring. Remember it was your idea to come here."

"Aye aw'right, but there must have been something exciting happened during the war, I'mean it lasted 5 years!"

A slow smile crossed Angela's lips.

"This book here says that maest things were rationed during the War; maybe people weren't allowed to do anything exciting without permission."

"A'h come on noo lassies, I don't know who has been telling you about the War, but they must have been living through a different one from me if there was no excitement."

Both girls looked at the man who stood in front of them. He was wearing his hat and scarf even though it was quite warm in the library. He rolled back and forth on his heels. His hands were stuffed hard down into the front pocket of his jacket, were pushed so far down that you could clearly make out the imprints of his knuckles.

Angela recognised him as one of her neighbours who stayed a few closes down from her house.

"Oh! hello Mr McIntosh. Were you in the War, then?"

"Mr McIntosh! Bobby's ma name hen. Aye I was in the War a'right and I liked it; but I was a daft boy then."

"What was it like then? We've been trying to find something interesting but these books have only got boring dates and names of battles. How did you get involved?"

"Aye, were ye forced to go, whit is it? Drifted in?"

"Drafted," said Angela.

"No! no need for that, I was glad to go. I thought it was a chance to see a bit of the world, as well as daein' ma bit to beat the Germans of course."

"Were ye no' scared then?" asked Diane.

Bobby turned to answer her and leaned in closer as if sharing a secret.

"Here, I'll tell you something. I was less scared of going to fight the Germans than I was about facing my auld Ma after I had joined up. Chased me up our street, hitting me with a pot and wouldnae speak to me for days."

Diane was in fits of laughter and turned to Angela and said

"That sounds jist like your Ma and Da!"

"It dis a bit din't it. Just a pity ma Da cannae get away so easy. So you were quite happy to go off to war then Bobby?" said a slightly embarassed Angela trying to change the subject.

"It must have been a bit frightening having to leave hame and all the people ye knew to go and get shot at?"

Bobby gripped both corners of the table and struck a pose as if he was about to give a speech. He shared with the girls tales of his Army training, how exciting and new it all was and how he kept in touch with home through letters from his family.

"I remember once a letter from my sister telling me about the bombing of Clydebank. Aye, I recall thinking that I was probably safer in the training camp; 'cause we stayed in Clydebank then, ye know."

"Bombing! in Clydebank, you mean the Germans flew over here and bombed us? Yer Kiddin'! I thought it was only London that got bombed,"

"Oh no! They hit us as well, lit up the whole city so people say."

"Whitfur?"

"The shipyards of course! They wanted to destroy the ships that we were building there."

"Haud on," said Angela "Ye mean, the Germans flew over here to bomb the ships that were were building to fight them ... cheating bastards! Sorry Mr McIntosh!"

"That's okay hen, that's exactly what they were; but it's the kind of thing that happens during War."

"This War caper might no' have been as boring as we thought," giving a nod in Bobby's direction. Angela urged Diane to keep him talking.

"So were you in a lot of fighting Bobby? Because we need some help with our homework."

"I'm your man hen. How can I help?" replied Bobby, standing just a little straighter than before.

Angela asked him what it was like when it was over and how he felt coming home. Bobby took a breath and with a voice that was a mix of passion and regret began saying,

"It was good! We felt we had achieved something, and I still feel we did; coming hame felt great as well, but it had changed or maybe it was me that had changed, but it was different anyway. There was a lot of excitement then as well, people had been living with the war for so long they were eager to get back to living some kind of normal life". His voice increased just a little and he began tapping the table quite forcefully with his finger,." And we had great hopes for the future then. There's no' a lot of that about nowadays!"

Just then one of the librarians casually passed and without actually saying anything, managed to make Bobby feel that he was making too much noise. He paused for a moment and then said, half to himself,

"You girls might know my grandson George?"

"He wis in my sisters' year at school."

"Aye, well he could tell you how exciting and bloody scary war is. Just now he's in the Gulf, fighting, and I know he would rather be here."

"He's only about 19 as well in't he?"

"Aye, only a boy, Bobby sighed." "Anyway have you got enough notes for your work now girls?"

"Plenty Bobby," Angela enthused. "You're 10 times better than the books in here. If we hidnae met you, we'd have nothing tae write. Thanks!"

Straightening up and putting his cap on, Bobby madeto leave, but he stopped, turned to the girls. "Could I ask you a favour girls? When you hand in your work to your teacher, ask him a question for me. Ask him to explain why Germany seems to have recovered from the War almost totally and is doing well; but I have to scrimp and save, fight for a decent pension and share the bookie's with fit young men, who even if they wanted to, couldn't find jobs? Will you do that for me?"

"Nae problem, Bobby," said Angela.

As Bobby left, Angela saw him for the first time , not as the person who had done and seen so much but just as an old man, like any other. When they were asked to leave at closing, instead of going back to Diane's house, Angela wanted to go home and finish the homework.

"Okay," said Diane, giving her a weird look, surprised at the idea of Angela actually wanting to do schoolwork.

"See ye t'morra."

Angela lifted her head from the notebook. The sound of the 10 o'clock news had disturbed her. Surprised at how fast the time had passed, she watched the report of the fighting in Kuwait. Thinking of how the fighting would affect those involved and the country itself, she took out the piece of paper with Bobby's question on it. Angela remembered how forgotten Bobby felt and wondered if those in the Gulf would be treated the same way.

Turning her gaze from the T.V., she spoke to her dad who had been sitting cursing the news and steadily getting angrier.

"Did ye know that George MacIntosh is fighting over there Da?"

"Is that no terrible! A young boy like that being forced to go and risk his life over the price of oil!"

Angela was getting used to these outbursts and the way her dad would lose his temper over simple things. She didn't really want to continue with the conversation, but knew that he would only brood if left alone.

"There's nae need to get so upset, Da, and anyway who says he wis forced to go? He wisnae drafted, I mean naebody made him join the army."

Her dad pulled back his lips in a way that she had only seen a few times before and one that made him look quite fierce.

"He may as well have been drafted, wee yin. The Army was the boy's only hope of getting a job and now he might die as a result!"

"Aw don't be so dramatic, Da!"

"Angela, I'm no' just being dramatic. I know what it's like to be so desperate for work. That any job, even a dangerous one will do. If the Army would take me I would probably join myself.

"I didnae think you were really interested in working anymore!"

Her dad gave a stifled laugh.

"Oh I want to work but I think you have more chance of getting a job than I have, or you would if you took more interest in your school work."

"Och don't start again, eh!" Angela groaned but this time his moaning didn't sound so silly. She had discovered that studying could relate to real people and things that were happening in the world, and if the choice was study or become like her mum and dad then....

"Da, could you set the alarm so that I can get up for school t'morra?"

James Hunter

Ambition

There is a place that no-one knows
That is the place where the moneytree grows
If you're a man who's in the know
Then you'll know just where to go
To see a friend in the city
Soon you'll find you're sitting pretty
He can teach you to screw somebody
Never mind if your hands get bloody
The knife you use, just use again
To tear the backs and cut the throats
Be a big man get the groats.

Anguish

Compel me to scribe a point of
ink to the virgin paper of the mind.
My soul is not a free thing
it does not soar it does not
fly to heights unknown.

Alone it sits inside the room
of loneliness..

It calls inside the cellars of my mind.
To hear the shriek,
the scrape of nails on walls...

Who Cares?

Welcome to the party, welcome to the house of joy
You shall have lots of fun this night
Cos you're a girl and he's a boy
Take the pills and take the booze
The two of you have minds to lose
Dance and dance the night away
Gonna have fun any which way
Take the drinks, more and more
Who cares what happens, you know life stinks
You're getting nearer and nearer to the brink
You're only seventeen, but you know where you've been
You're not bothered where you going, cos there's
Nothing left to live for
You make the rounds of the boys and they treat you
Like a toy
You hear the laughs and the sniggers, you realise
You have it figured
All the funtimes, well they're just lies
There's nothing but hurt
In the house of joy
Welcome to the party.

Mary Maghee

Raintown

"In a raintown, raintown, raintown, rain down on all those tired eyes and tears and frowns."

The words of Deacon Blue's song keeps running through my mind. The traffic's very busy, we're going across the bridge, everyone is in a hurry. The old woman standing at the pelican waiting to cross the road, she looks so sad. Where is she headed? She's drenched.

It's coming down in sheets, battering the roof, the sound makes me feel as if I'm sitting in a tin can. I wish they'd stop talking. Can't they see how frightened I am? She's very young, wise, and smart in her blue starched uniform. Will she be able to cope if it happens again? She's lying so still in my arms, so peaceful, my beautiful baby. The heat from her body burning my heart as I hold her close to me. Is she breathing? I wish John were here, I need him, his support. I need to cry to release this fear screaming inside me. Don't cry, Mary, don't cry. Bite your lip. I feel so inadequate. I didn't know what to do. I held her in my arms as her limbs jerked so violently, watching her little body retching out of control, yet asleep. Please wake up. Cry. Do something.

He's just sitting there, dressed in his green paramedic overalls. Does he know how I feel, care? Why don't they reassure me? Why don't they tell me she's fine instead of making idle talk? I don't give a damn what they're having for lunch or if she's going to the cinema this evening. What will the evening have in store for me? I suppose they're used to this, it's an everyday occurrence to them, all in a day's work. That's not fair. They work real hard, they can't be unaffected by all the sorrow they come across. They must have to take it on board and cope.

The paramedic looks prepared for most emergencies, surrounded by his hi-tech equipment on wheels. If only I had their knowledge and ability to help others. What time is it? Must be around nine. The office workers with their briefcases are scurrying about, dodging the puddles. Children on their way to school laughing as their umbrellas fly inside out. How much longer will it take? Traffic jams, rain rain rain. I'm so tired. She was fine yesterday. Maybe she woke in the night and I didn't hear her. If I hadn't been working I wouldn't have been so tired. John didn't mention that she was off colour last night when I got home. She must have been all right then.

The rain has stopped or down to a drizzle. There's the gate in sight. The doors of my tin can are opening. The cold morning air comes rushing in and she gasps as the wind catches her breath. I carry her into the reception, wiping the raindrops from her forehead. Her eyes are open, her lovely blue eyes so clear. What a beautiful smile my baby has. It's all right Patricia. Here's your daddy coming. Everything is going to be Okay and when you're well again, I'll put on your welly boots and you can splash about in the puddles.

CATH CRAIG

ENVIRONMENTALLY FRIENDLY

Bricks and rubble, worn-eaten lumber,
Smelly old mattresses, meant for slumber,
Empty crisp pokes, sticky with glue,
Cardboard boxes, someone's old loo,
Broken-down tellies, a cracked oil sump,
I'm not describing a rubbish dump.

Shopping trolleys and old tin cans,
Rusting cars and burnt out vans,
Bicycle pieces and poly bags,
Junkies' needles and blood-stained rags,
Broken glass and razor blades,
All things found on the Cathkin Braes.

Glasgow's Alive

Glasgow's alive and kicking,
Glasgow's alive and stabbing,
Glasgow's alive and shooting
Heroin into its veins.

Glasgow's alive and workless,
Glasgow's alive and poor,
Glasgow's alive and struggling
Tae keep the wolf fae the door.

Glasgow's alive and green,
Glasgow's alive and blue,
Glasgow's alive and bigoted
Baith fenian and loyal and true.

Glasgow's alive and decadent,
Glasgow's alive and corrupt,
Glasgow's alive and exploited,
But her people will not be shut up.
So Glasgow's alive and flourishing,

Bells ringing, birds singing,
Fish swimming, trees growing,
In spite of the bastards.

Out Of The Darkness

He didn't want to open his eyes, but slowly, painfully, his eyelids opened. There was darkness all around, a blackness so dense that he felt the hairs on the back of his neck rise.

I can't see, I'm blind, I can't fucken see! an inner voice kept repeating. His first thought was for his garden. He wouldn't be able to see his roses again, his pride and joy, winning him prizes year after year at the village fair. He had lavished all his spare time on it and felt that it had repaid him twofold with its bright colours and heady scents. Just the thing a man needed when he returned home from a hard shift in the twilight existence of the mine. He tried to picture his garden, home and family but no matter how hard he tried, he couldn't recall them clearly. Don't panic, he told himself, its's only the darkness of the mine. I'll soon be able to see. Then he remembered the explosion.

He could still hear that thundering roar. It had pierced his eardrums like a dentist's drill hitting a raw nerve in a tooth. The rush of air and dust which followed had picked him off his feet and slammed him spreadeagled against the coal face. The choking dust invaded his lungs forcing the life-giving air from his chest. He blacked out. He had not felt the heat of the flames as they licked hungrily across his unconscious body, nor felt the pit prop fall across his legs and pelvis pinning him to the mine floor.

He came round slowly, his ears still ringing, the only sound he could hear apart from his own heartbeat. Every part of his body ached, but the pain in his face, arms and hands where he had been burned was the worst. The rest of his body was bruised but not burnt. His helmet and thick canvas overalls had protected him as they had been designed to do. He tried to sit up, but the great weight lying across his lower body made this impossible. Gingerly he ran his fingers over his upper arms and chest, feeling for any broken bones. Beads of sweat fringed his upper lip as blistered fingers caught on the hard charred cloth of his overalls, bringing this examination to an abrupt end.

He could move his legs and feet slightly , so his back was OK. He must have landed in a hollow or something because the pit prop lying across him didn't seem as heavy as he would have expected. He tried to wriggle out from underneath it, but couldn't get any purchase. He remembered the crane flies he used to catch when he was young, pinning them to the table by their legs. Now he knew how they had felt.

The ringing in his ears was getting less and he could hear low moans coming from all around him. There had been forty five men in this part of the pit when the explosion happened. Their shift finished, they had been on their way to the top. He started calling his workmates by name, like a teacher taking the register in class. Some called back to him, others just moaned. A few didn't respond at all. Were they dead or just unconscious? Perhaps they'd escaped and were on the other side of the rockfall that had him trapped.

A voice to his left told him to shut up, to conserve what little air they had. God! he hadn't thought about that! He began to feel claustrophobic. He sniffed the air like a dog. It was full of strange smells that he tried to identify. The aroma of roast pork puzzled him. Horrified he realised it was the smell of burning flesh, human flesh. Suddenly his mouth filled with vomit and he was sick. He sniffed again. Was that gas he could smell? Or was the air turning stale, heralding a slow death by suffocation? Don't think about death, he told himself. Think about life and rescue.

His mind drifted back to the conversation he had with his mother at breakfast that morning. He told her about the offer of a job as a gardener at the big house. The offer had come from his Lordship himself who wanted a young man to look after his gardens. His present gardener, Jenkins, was getting too old to do all the work himself and the new man would be trained to take over from Jenkins, when he retired later that year. It would mean moving out of the tied cottage they lived in now, into one on the estate. He had promised his Lordship that he would discuss it with his mother and sisters and give him a decision later that week.

His mother hadn't been too pleased at the idea of moving out of her cottage. After all she'd stayed there all her married life. When his father had died last year he had been working in the mine with his only son, so the family had been allowed to stay in their tied cottage. He could understand her reluctance to leave the only home they had ever shared. After much cajoling he had managed to win her over to the idea. He had planned to tell the mine foreman at the end of this shift that he would be leaving the mine the next day. If things went wrong and the rescue party didn't reach them on time, his mother and sisters would be without a roof over their heads. Please god get me out of this airless tomb in time.

The drip, drip, drip of water. God he was thirsty. He could murder a pint.

That would soon clear the dust from his throat. He ran his tongue over his cracked lips, imagining the taste of ice-cold frothy beer. Instead, coming from a cut just below his nose, salty blood filled his mouth.

How long would it take the rescue squad to reach them? He strained his ears hoping to hear the strike of their picks on rock. The klaxons would be sounding over the mine workings now, and in the village mothers and daughters, wives and sweethearts would have hurried up the hill, all the time praying that their menfolk were safe. They would be standing up there now, some waiting for news of their men. Others, relieved that theirs were safe, would stay around to comfort the less fortunate. As in times past they would rally round and help in any way they could. It was a close-knit community, built up over many years of adversity. His mother and sisters would be there, arms around each other. It was worse for them, he thought. After all he knew he was still alive. They didn't.

He lay there for what seemed like years, but was in fact several hours, drifting in and out of consciousness. He didn't hear the strike of picks on rock. When he felt gentle hands pulling his battered and blackened body out from beneath the pit prop, he groaned and opened his eyes. A disembodied voice reassured him that he was going to be alright, that they would have him up top in no time. Someone else wetted his lips with water and he caught some on his tongue. It tasted like nectar as it trickled down his parched throat. Slowly, carefully, they lifted him on to a stretcher and started the journey up to the top. He could tell when they were near the ground. The air became sweeter, cooler. He sucked the air deep into his lungs, feeling new life surge through him. As they carried him out of the mine, the sun was warm against his skin. He blinked rapidly as the sudden light dazzled him, but he didn't mind. He could see! His burns didn't seem to hurt as much, he even managed to crack a joke with his rescuers, demanding to know if he would get double time for working an extra shift on a Sunday.

His mother and sisters crowded round the stretcher, kissing and hugging him gently. As she bent over him he could taste his mother's tears. She told him that his Lordship had sent a message to her, saying that the gardening job would be held for him until he was fit. They were to move into the new cottage as soon as they could pack up their few belongings. He was alive thank god, he was alive! And he would never have to descend into the darkness again.

Eddie Graham

Cardboard Box Hotel

I'm sleeping on the Southbank, cause I've no place else to go.
There's cardboard boxes everywhere, homeless row by row.
I sold my watch for a pizza, now I've nothing left to sell,
so I'm sleeping on the Southbank, in the Cardboard Box Hotel.

London, rich man's city, where the rich get richer still,
poor get even poorer, paying rich man's phoney bills.
They rip me off for everything, living life is hell,
sleeping rough in cartons, in the Cardboard Box Hotel.

Rising in the morning, the mist hangs like a veil,
my bones are creaking hinges, and I slop out in a pail.
Matchstick men like Lowrie paints them, girls like Little Nell
Queing up with boxes, in the Cardboard Box Hotel.

Big new fancy jaguars, when yuppies come to call.
They urinate their champagne on the boxes by the wall,
and though Policemen saw them, they say they cannot tell,
if they urinated on me, in the Cardboard Box Hotel.

The Social does not know me, and the pains of living show.
My head's sore and my feet on fire, tramping to & fro.
When Jesus wrote my horoscope, he bid me fare-thee-well,
and dumped me with the cats & rats, in the Cardboard Box Hotel.

Some folks cannot take it, their hearts break and they cry.
The old folk never make it, they just go to sleep and die.
Great land of hope & glory, I've learned this lesson well,
the hope that's for the homeless, is a Cardboard Box Hotel.

Looking Back on Tomorrow

The common market's booming,
the foodstuff piles and gluts,
the ones who said Don't be afraid,
are introducting CUTS.

The pound rate keeps on falling,
the trend goes down in spurts,
we're in the red and being bled,
by introducing CUTS.

We're cutting education,
the school and college shuts,
and now instead of being well read,
they're introducing CUTS.

They're cutting back house building,
to caravans and huts,
the future's dead for newly weds,
Thro' introducing CUTS.

They're cutting back on beef-steak,
to Soya beans and nuts,
and tho' you dread being underfed,
they're introducing CUTS

THEY borrow tens of millions,
to balance budgets BUT,
I heard it said, the interest's spread,
for years and years and years ahead;

By that time friend we'll all be dead,
have sold our souls for foreign aid,
and economic CUTS.

Christine Quarrell

2 Haiku

Starlings scattered
like currants
across
a doughy sky

sticky lolly buds
bursting into spring

Ma's Here

Shush shush ma ain wee wean
Ma's here   yir safe again
Da's away tae the pub
Shush shush   here's yir grub.

Dinna girn   dinna greet
Look I've shoes fur yir feet.
Come oan   nae sulkin noo
I've a few bob tae next buroo.

Sexism

Patriarchal tea
steak for him
eggs for me.

Working Class Women

WORKING CLASS WOMEN
MEN OUCH OW !
KING ASS WO
ORK ORK ORK ORK ORK
LASS ME ME ME ME I
N IN IN IN WOM B
CORK CLING WING...
RING OOO O OOO O OOO
WO WO WO WO WO MEN
KOR CSS CSS CSS mMMm
SAL CAS SAS NEW NEW NEW...
...ING GIRNING NOG NOG NOG GO...
SAC SAC DAC WO M EN
NEM SA MEN SA MEN SA NEM SA SASASA
WOE OWE OWE NO NO NO NOOOOOOOO
WON WO WOM WOS WOL A A WOL
WOC GOW WO I OWR WO-WO-WO-WO-M-MM-MMM-WOME-
WOMEE
WOMEN

FEMALE

FEMALE, FEMALE
FE MALE
MALE MALE MALE
MA MA MA MA MA MA
HOW MANY SUGARS DAE A TAKE IN   MA
MA......MA   MA.....MA   MA.....MA
AM A MALE ME
EE EE EEEEEEEEE
FE FO FI FUM
I SMELL THE BLOOD OF A WO...........
MAN
FEEL FEEL FEEL..?
ALE ALE ALE
MORE ALE WENCH
FI-FI   FEE FEE   FI-FI
MM M MM M MMMM
EMA E MA EE MMA !
BRING MA GLESSES
FEM-FALE

PLEASE SIR ?

DILYS ROSE

GYNAE

The face was too big, as if the head had been rolled flat. Blurred; the eyes and mouth just dark smudges. And too close, almost touching her own. All she could see. Her hands went out to push the face away but as she reached out, it backed off, ballooning up into the darkness.

- Just checking.

Night staff. In dark blue. The ones in white took temperatures, blood pressures, urine samples and sat on your bed with a clipboard and a list of questions. The ones in yellow brought clean sheets and tea, if you didn't have NIL BY MOUTH above your bed. Pale green for the theatre crew, plus masks and non-slip clogs. One of them held your hand, the others horsed around, while they knocked you out. They did their business while you were off in limbo land. The jolly butchers. What did the bluecoats do?

- Alright?

There was a smell, not a bad smell, familiar but she couldn't put a name to it. A free-floating memory. No connection, no link to a particular person, place, time. She rubbed her cheek against the pillow, trying to identify the smell. The night nurse must have taken her movement to be a nod because she moved off, a smile spreading like a stain across the lower part of her face. The soles of her shoes made a sucking noise as they detached themselves from the lino.

Calomine? Calendula? Something medicinal but gentle, a balm, not at all like the harsh hospital smells. Camphor, Camomile, she had the feeling it was something beginning with Ca. Ca Ca Ca Ca.....If she could name the smell, she'd be nearer to pinning it down but she went blank after camomile and that wasn't it. Whatever it was, it was comforting and she was in need of comfort. She wasn't allright but neither was anybody else in the ward and she wouldn't be as bad as some. The nurse was out of earshot. She'd have to raise her voice to be heard, which was bound to disturb other patients.

Was there a bell to press? On the wall behind her bed were a couple of unmarked buttons but nobody'd told her what they were for. After they'd taken her particulars - and asked her for the nth time if she was sure she wanted to go ahead with it - they'd just left her there to wait for her turn to be wheeled along to theatre. Her mouth opened and made the shape of NURSE but not even a whisper came out. Across the aisle, a woman howled. It was the bleak, naked cry of someone trapped in a bad dream.

She'd been sleeping, dreaming maybe, she couldn't remember, but it had been deep and soothing, the kind of sleep people talked about in books but didn't, in her experience, happen so often. A total escape from awareness. She owed it to the little sturdy nurse - bobbed hair, specs, the trace of an Irish accent - and her needle. She remembered the chill of meths on her skin, the steel point push firmly into her backside, a brief swelling as the morphine sank in, the seductive rush of numbing warmth.

How long had she slept? How many hours had passed? That was what mattered, passing the hours, days, god help them weeks, staring at the telly or the ceiling, using up the time in baths, meals, medication, sleep. In Gynae people didn't talk much and didn't ask what you were in for. Too touchy an area: terminations and blocked tubes, women getting rid of babies, women desperate to conceive. If they could have done a swap...

Her back-to-front gown felt damp. She slid her hand over the sheet. Damp also. Maybe just sweat. Maybe that was all it was but she'd have to look, to check because the nurse hadn't. The light switch was in an awkward place, high on the wall behind the bed. She had to turn over on to her side and hoist herself up, supported by an arm which felt as if the bones had dissolved, as if it hadn't been used for a very long time. The stitches tugged as she lunged for the light. God Almightly. Worse than before. A flood.

She sat up in bed, holding the sodden red sheet away from her matching gown, staring at the strange brightness of the blood. How could it be her own, all that from a small incision at the navel? She looked like one of the battle victims she'd seen on the lunchtime news, when there was no lunch because they hadn't done her yet, hadn't opened her up. To get away from the tormenting smell of food which wafted into the ward from the corridor, she'd moved through to the patient's sitting room. Nothing like NIL BY MOUTH above your bed to whet the appetite.

An auxiliary had been dusting seats.

- Glad I don't work *there* she'd said, as footage from yet another war-torn city was blasted across the screen. Bombs and bloody corpses. Hospitals bursting at the seams. - What a world, eh? The things people do to each other. Never watch the news. Gets me down, so it does. *Hello* magazine, that's my cup of tea. Everybody's happy, that's what I like to see. Gives you a wee lift. Want a loan of this week's issue?

She'd said no to *Hello.*

Like a moth, the night nurse fluttered towards the light and drew the curtains round her bed. More red. Red and pink stripes to stare at while the nurse went off without a word, to find something or someone. At the far end of the ward a cistern hissed. Did she need to pee? The last time they'd made her use a commode. The swaying curtains were making her nauseous.

She shouldn't still be here, wouldn't have been if things had gone to plan. She'd told the nurse, the sturdy one with the needle. She'd told her she had to get home, the kids would be upset, she'd promised them a bedtime story. An anyway she couldn't waste any more time on all this, she'd have to be back on her feet the next day, or the day after at the outside, have to be fit for work. If she took the injection she couldn't go home...

- One thing at a time, Christine, said the nurse, the only one out of everybody she'd seen who called her by her first name. It had seemed more caring somehow and she had been in a state, the pain severe and the morphine had taken it away, taken everything away for a while. Even now she still felt detached from her body, distant, except for the wound. All she felt in touch with was the wound, invisible under a sodden dressing, only the incision at the navel linked her with her body.

A low rumble of trolley wheels. The curtains parting like the Red Sea. Another face. Yellow coat. Armful of starched linen.

- What a state you're in, said the auxiliary, sighing at the sight of it, her, and she felt embarrassed by the mess, the trouble, about having to sit on a chair while a stranger changed her bed, covered the sodden dressing with a fresh lint pad - We'll leave that to the doctor - and dressed her in a clean gown. Like a baby, a bloody baby. She'd gone through a load of linen, made extra work for everybody.

Something had been taken away. That had been the point of the hospital visit, to take something, no, the *possibility* of something away from the invisible regions of her body. That had been done. She had been done. Doctored. She'd volunteered. The decision had been made under no pressure from anyone and it had seemed like a good idea, a practical one at any rate, one which would simplify the future, make it manageable. But something else had been taken away.

A white-coated nurse breezed through the curtains, followed by a young male doctor, in theatre green. He held out his hand to her but before she realised that she was meant to shake it, the hand had been retracted. She could feel a wild giggle bubbling up from the pit of her stomach, trying to free itself, to erupt into the sleeping ward. She mustn't laugh. It would hurt to laugh and anyway, it wasn't funny, there was nothing at all to laugh at.

But God, he was so young to be left in charge. Just a boy, white-faced under the light, unruly red curls falling into his eyes. Not exactly Doctor Kildare. As a kid she'd watched the debonair Chamberlain on telly and - along with thousands or maybe millions of other female viewers - fantasised about being laid up with some critical, (but not disfiguring) injury and coaxed back to health by a concerned and attentive Kildare.

A lot of bloody nonsense. Nobody in their right mind would want to meet a man they fancied under these conditions. A woman, even a very young woman would have been better. A woman would have made more sense. Why were there so many men in Gynae? How could a man decide what best to do with bits he didn't have? And what in god's name attracted them to specialise in that department? Were they all perverts or what?

The smell was still there. Maybe it was in the linen. Knowing what it was, wasn't going to help any but it was something to think about, something else. Maybe it was in the air. The flowers? Plenty flowers about the place, though none at her own bedside. She'd had no visitors. No need, she'd be in and out the same day, that was the plan. But the plan had fallen through and when they decided - the smarmy young surgeon who cracked jokes about bimbos and bikini lines and the nice nurse with the needle - when they decided to keep her in overnight, she'd wished to god that one of those fit people who filled up the ward after the evening meal with chat and chocolates, was there to visit *her*. But no flowers. Elsewhere she liked them; in the wild, in a garden, a vase on the kitchen table. But not in hospital. There was something stiff and lifeless about the florist's sprays, the functional bunches of cheery daisies, tight, fleshy rosebuds and papery carnations. Carnations. Could it be the carnations?

She felt stupid being wheeled through the ward flat on her back, tried to sit up, was gently but firmly restrained by the nurse, put in her place, in the hands of two tired-looking kids....

Notices in the corridor. NO SMOKING. GIVE UP SMOKING. PATIENT'S CHARTER. What did that say? She'd read it through that morning as she waited to be admitted, waited to hand over her body..... courteous..... prompt.....ensure. What was it that they would ensure? What was it that she had a right to expect?

The overhead light in the theatre was weak and ineffectual, sick-looking. Gone the bright daytime buzz of the operating room, gone the loud, hairy porter who showed off his tattoos, leered at the *ladies* and jollied them along to the chopping block. At night the room was grey and dreary and deserted.

She was rolled off the trolley on to the table, a surprisingly narrow metal and rubber affair, and left on her own again. It was the way of it. Entrances and exits. And then the voices off - whispers, laughter, the well world going on as usual on the other side of the curtain. Had they gone for a bloody tea-break?

She could do with a drink. Nothing all day. NIL BY MOUTH. A drink would make her feel better. And a bite to eat. Bread and water would do fine. If she could get hold of the one who'd changed her bed.... Why hadn't she thought to ask at the time? She was the one to ask. Tea was one of her duties. No point in asking the wrong person, the doctor, say. Doctors didn't deal with tea.

There was something worrying about the way the two of them were passing instruments back and forward, and all that rattling and clinking. It seemed..... experimental, like kids making up a game, a kind of medical Mad Hatter's Tea Party. The nurse couldn't find the bloody scissors. The doctor was holding up a length of catgut which looked like a guitar string. He was squinting at the stuff with the curiosity people show for something they've never seen before. She felt horribly alert. She'd seen more than enough and they hadn't even started yet. If they'd just given her a bloody general like the first time, instead of a local, all she'd know would be a fizzing tingle in the veins, then blackout.

But it was the nurse who blacked out, just after the doctor peeled off the dressing. He held it out to the nurse for her to dispose of but she shook her head. Her eyelids flickered rapidly. Her face turned the colour of the walls. She stepped clear of the operating table and flopped on to the floor. The doctor gawped at the body on the floor and the body on the table, stupefied by panic. The desire to run away was written all over him, yet he did nothing except stare at his hands as if he were counting them and wondering, Why so few?

Beneath her dressing the blood had pooled thick and dark and in an alarming quantity. As the doctor dithered between cleaning up the patient and resuscitating the nurse, she lay on the table and looked up at the ceiling. Again a giggle - or was it a scream? - bubbled up from her guts.

- Can I do anything to help? she said. Help was needed and at that moment she was the only person available to supply it.

CONTRIBUTORS

Thomas Anderson: was a member of the songwriters' workshop at C Sharp Music Factory before it disbanded. ***Peter Arthur:*** is 38 and lives and works in Castlemilk. ***Lesley Benzie:*** grew up in Aberdeen and now lives in the Castlemilk area with her family. ***G.L. Buglass:*** was born in Glasgow in 1932, is married with 3 grown up children. Civil Service Commission Certificate (English) gained during RAF service in 1952. Interested in poetry since childhood. 'Topical' poetry published at various times in the press. Ultimately hopes for publication of collected poems. ***Colette Coen:*** is an English graduate of Glasgow University with a post graduate diploma from RGIT. Spent time in Aberdeen and Dumfries thenreturned to Glasgow. Has been writing short stories for three years and, in 1990, won the Whitbread Essay Prize. ***Cath Craig:*** a Castlemilk 'lifer' who likes the place. Community activist in recent years and still sees some hope for the future. Aged over 21 and mother of three grown ups. Took up writing last year and is still wondering why. A founder member of the library-based Castlemilk Writers' group. ***Jim Craig:*** Ex-paratrooper, ex-nurse, ex-housing and community worker. Long term resident of Castlemilk who still sees the place through rose-tinted glasses and likes to see the potential rather than the reality of the place. Been writing for about 3 years and aims to be good at it one day. ***Austin Docherty:*** lives and studies in Castlemilk. ***Michael Geddes:*** is 45 and has been writing, on and off, for 15 years. To date he's completed 2 plays, 12 short stories and about 30 poems. Currently working on a novel. ***Rosina Gilmour:*** joined the Castlemilk Writers' group at the library early this year and found her life again enriched by the resources of the community. Is delighted that some of her efforts - so much encouraged by the group - have been included in a book associated with the area. ***Eddie Graham:*** is 68, an ex-commando who spent many years in working class voluntary organisations. Found so many stupid officials in positions of authority, he's convinced 'they tell you anything if you're stupid enough to believe them'. Writes poetry to relieve his contempt for such. He's concerned for the poor and underpriveleged. ***Eileen Hart:*** is a 38 year old housewife, lives in Glasgow and has three children. An ex-taxi and bus driver, she recently had her first story accepted by New Fiction Pbs, 'Shorts from Scotland', due out in Ocotber 1992 ***Jackie Hodgman:*** Born Glasgow 1953. One grown up son. Started writing three years ago, although always thought about it and has dabbled since a child. Hundreds of unfinished projects lying around her desk and brain. Ambition: to be a renaissance woman and do everything reasonably well: Feart in case her many reads Rumpelstiltskin and says, 'Oh and you used to be such a good poet!' ***James Hunter:*** has been writing on and off, (mostly off), for 8 or 9 years and tends to write in a 'heavy' sort of style, not because he likes it overmuch. It is just the way it flows. Is also a member of the progressive folk/blues duo Mercy.

John McGarrigle: is 37 and has lived most of his life in Castlemilk. Began writing 7 years ago when he joined the WEA Castlemilk Writers' Workshop. Has since published several poems and stories, including his own collection of poetry, Glasgow's McGarrigle. ***Mary Maghee:*** Married with three children. Lived in Castlemilk for thirty five years. While studying for Higher English as a mature student at Castlemilk High School she discovered an enjoyment and therapeutic benefit of writing. She continues to enjoy education and aims to study for a degree in Diagnostic Radiography at University next year. ***John McGinty:*** Born in Rutherglen 1949. Resident in Castlemilk nine years. Married to Cathie, a local lass. Two beautiful sons, Steven and John. Took up writing last year. Influences - Norman McCaig, W. S. Graham, Burns Singer and Tom Leonard. ***Teresa Meagher:*** born Teresa Giblin in Shettleston. Married with 8 grown up children and 12 grandchildren who enjoy getting together as much as possible. Prefers not to be parochial in her writing and admits to enjoying slices of the good life. Would like a modern flat....not in Castlemilk. ***Margaret Millmaker:*** hobbies include writing, classical music and rock 'n' roll. Has been writing for years but only got involved in writers' groups within the last 3 years. Enjoys the groups as they give her inspiration and ideas. ***Ruziah Mohd*** *Nor:* mother of four who has been in Scotland for a year to accompany her student husband. The poems come from her first experience here of the Christmas and summer holidays, when she felt that, though they were welcomed, there was a certain unease and resentment attached to them. ***David Pearce:*** Bornin Rutherglen, 1973, and educated at Stonelaw High School. Due to illness since leaving school he has concentrated on writing but is also interested in classical guitar and art and hopes to pursue one of these interests as a career when he recovers fully. ***Alex Potts:*** Age 30, resident in Castlemilk. Qualified fashion technician. Founder member of WEA Castlemilk Writers' Workshop in 1983. One half of folk/blues duo **Mercy**, (formerly Drunken Donuts). Writes most of the material. Available for gigs. Known pseudo intellectual and also knows other people as well. Veri bag speler. Reads comics. ***Christine Quarrell:*** is 42, a working class mother strongly influenced by feminism and socialism. Passions are eating, poetry, photography, sons David (23), Greig (15) and my family and friends. Writing heals me, helps me express anger and happiness. We are all creative beings and creativity can be a weapon in the struggle for survival. ***Christine Stewart:*** is 34. Has enjoyed writing since primary school. Not particularly serious about it but very much enjoys trying to create pieces with a touch of humour. Her daughter gives her a lot of inspiration. ***Alex Telford:*** moved to Castlemilk in 1978 from Gorbals. Enjoyed time at Glenwood Secondary. Was unemployed for 5 years. Found way back to work through training and voluntary work. Interests include: God, live music of any kind, sign language and voluntary work.